The American Assembly, *Columbia University*

AUTOMATION

AND TECHNOLOGICAL CHANGE

Prentice-Hall, Inc., *Englewood Cliffs, N. J.*

A SPECTRUM BOOK

LIBRARY OF CONGRESS CATALOG CARD NO.: 62-17597

Printed in the United States of America

05498-C

Preface

The chapters in this volume, edited by John T. Dunlop, were not intended to provide a detailed program for private and public policies on automation and technological change. They were designated to eliminate some of the exaggeration, suspicion, and mystery that have surrounded the subject; to provide historical perspective and factual information as to the impact of automation and technological change; and to sharpen some of the central issues for public discussion.

The first discussion of this subject sponsored by The American Assembly took place May 3-6, 1962, in a national meeting at Arden House, on the Harriman (New York) Campus of Columbia University. The final report of that Assembly begins on page 175.

The views expressed herein are those of the individual authors and the participants and not of either The American Assembly, which by charter and legal limitation takes no position, or of the Maurice and Laura Falk Foundation, whose generous support made this Twenty-first American Assembly program possible.

Henry M. Wriston
President
The American Assembly

Since its establishment by Dwight D. Eisenhower at Columbia University in 1950, The American Assembly has held Assemblies of national leaders and has published books to illuminate issues of United States policy.

The Assembly is a national, non-partisan educational institution, incorporated under the State of New York. It was the official administrator of the President's Commission on National Goals, which reported to President Eisenhower late in 1960.

The Trustees of the Assembly approve a topic for presentation in a background book, authoritatively designed and written to aid deliberations at national Assembly sessions at Arden House, the Harriman Campus of Columbia University. These books are also used to support discussion at regional Assembly sessions and to evoke consideration by the general public.

All sessions of the Assembly, whether international, national or local, issue and publicize independent reports of conclusions and recommendations on the topic at hand. Participants in these sessions constitute a wide range of experience and competence.

Table of Contents

John T. Dunlop, Editor

Introduction:
Problems and Potentials

"The major domestic challenge of the Sixties," President Kennedy said at a press conference on February 15, 1962, is to "maintain full employment at a time when automation is replacing men." He said, "It is a fact that we have to find over a ten-year period 25,000 new jobs every week to take care of those displaced by machines and those who are coming into the labor market." James Reston of the *New York Times* commented that "machines are replacing everything in this country, except maybe pretty girls, and President Kennedy is worried about it."

The President's Advisory Committee on Labor-Management Policy, in its report on automation, issued January 11, 1962, well stated this challenge: "Our purpose, then, is to seek the course of action which will encourage essential progress in the form of automation and technological change, while meeting at the same time the social consequences such change creates." In a sentence this also defines the central issues of this American Assembly: (1) how to generate a higher rate of technological change, and (2) how to share the costs of the dislocations and the benefits of technological change.

Automation means many things to different people. In a rigorous and technical sense, it should refer only to those forms of technological change or mechanization which combine the elements of the computer, transfer

JOHN T. DUNLOP, *Professor of Economics at Harvard and Chairman of its Department of Economics, has served in various governmental capacities and with labor and management as a neutral. He was a public member of the Presidential Railroad Commission (1960-62); he is a public member of the Missile Sites Labor Commission and impartial chairman of the Construction Industry Joint Conference. Professor Dunlop is author of* Wage Determination Under Trade Unions; Collective Bargaining: Principles and Cases; Industrial Relations Systems; *(co-author);* Industrialism and Industrial Man *and other books and articles.*

1

devices, and automatic controls.[1] The central idea is that mechanical or chemical processes are directed, controlled, and corrected within limits automatically, that is, without further human intervention once the system is established. Automation may be applied generally in a factory, office or government defense facility. Its range varies considerably in that there are wide differences in the operations, the complexity of the instructions and the sorts of corrections or adjustments which may be made automatically. Automation may not be very new, even if rigorously defined, but its application has been so extended in recent years, and its potentials for the future are now so clear, that it has acquired new significance.

But for the purposes of private and public policy-making, a general view of technological change is likely to prove more useful than a restricted definition of automation. There are few, if any, statistical measures of the extent or rate of change in automation, using a rigorous definition. It is impossible to isolate the impact of automation from other forms of mechanization and technological change. Many of the policy problems and implications are undifferentiated and only matters of degree. Accordingly, the present volume is focused on the larger processes of technological change as well as on automation.

Generation of innovation and technological change

For most of human history, until very recently, invention was largely autonomous and dependent upon isolated individuals. As Professor Sumner Slichter said,

> Only such powerful drives as love of one's fellow men or the thirst for fame or glory or insatiable curiosity can explain the willingness to risk life or limb to make a desired discovery or to demonstrate that an invention would work. The history of medicine and aviation is full of such heroic efforts to make discoveries. . . . Since the chance was remote that the would-be inventors could achieve success, business concerns were unwilling to put resources at the disposal of researchers, and only a few more or less fanatical spirits were willing to devote their lives to technological research.[2]

But in the last few decades there has arisen an industry of discovery. The expenditures on research from private and public sources have risen from the order of half a billion to over ten billion dollars per year in the

[1] *Automation, A Report on the Technical Trends and Their Impact on Management and Labor,* Department of Scientific and Industrial Research, London, Her Majesty's Stationery Office, 1956.

[2] *Economic Growth in the United States, Its History, Problems and Prospects,* Louisiana State University Press, 1961, John T. Dunlop, ed.

past two decades. Substantial resources and large scale organizations are now devoted to invention.

> This accumulation of knowledge and improvements in methods of investigation has eventually made it possible to apply the economic calculus to research and to establish the new industry of discovery. . . . The essential point is that the cost, the chance of success, and the value of the results can be estimated with sufficient accuracy so that it can be decided in a more or less intelligent fashion, (1) how much money an enterprise may advantageously put into its research department, or (2) whether contracts for research may be made with outside agencies with a reasonable chance that the money will have been well spent.

The industry of discovery opens up a new vista of the long future in which substantial resources in increasing amounts are devoted systematically to what E. E. Morrison has called "the art of organized forcing of technological change," to reshaping the physical environment of mankind and to providing increased living standards and cultural opportunities. The relations between research and technology on the one hand and increased productivity on the other are not simple. But the rise of the industry of discovery suggests that we should be able to look forward to doubling productivity and living standards more frequently than in 24 years, at the current rate of 3 per cent per year. It should not be too much to look forward to the day when productivity increases at such a rate (5 per cent a year) that these standards are doubled every fifteen years. These potentials underscore the common gains to be shared by increasing productivity and the possibilities of insuring adequately those who bear the costs of the adverse initial impacts of some technological changes.

The industry of discovery also raises a host of issues and questions which are slowly coming to the fore. What should be the size of this industry and how fast should it grow? To what extent should the industry be private, to what extent public, and to what extent non-profit with various forms of organization as to finance, management and control? What is to determine the priorities of research of the industry of discovery? To what extent shall the direction of invention be left to the individual spirit and curiosity, to the market, and to what extent directed by priorities established by what bodies? What is to be the relation of the industry of discovery to the universities, and what problems and adaptations are created for the universities by large-scale private, public and non-profit research organizations? How can we increase creativity, and how are we to avoid the large losses which arise when high potential talents are wasted through loss of opportunity or misuse? The questions are so significant a part of automation and technological change that they cannot be ignored. The size, the character and the rate of growth of the industry of discovery are fundamental to the rate of technological change. The chapter by Francis Bello is concerned with some of these problems.

Technological change is not to be identified with science and discovery. In the words of President Stratton of M.I.T., "Science gives us knowledge and power of action. It tells us what we *can* do. . . ." Research seeks out the possible and the more or less practicable; technological change, however, reflects the actual adoption of new methods and products; it is the triumph of the new over the old in the test of the market and the budget.

Technological change, apart from discovery, is a complex economic and social process which is influenced by a range of decisions by business enterprises, labor organizations and workers, national and local governmental agencies, the education system, households, and by the values and attitudes of the whole community. No single body makes a decision as to the rate of technological change in the society; no law can increase it by simple decree.

In order to increase the rate of technological change, new decisions are required at many points in the community. Any one group may retard the process, but the contribution of all is required if the community is to accelerate the rate of change. In a democracy it is accordingly imperative to explore the terms on which all groups may be encouraged to enhance their contribution to technological advance and to reduce their opposition to change. The response of various groups depends greatly on the impacts of technological change, including the allocation of the costs of the dislocations and the benefits.

Impacts of technological change

The effects of technological change have been a matter of controversy since the early days of the Industrial Revolution. In part, this diversity of views reflected the fact that technological change often had different effects on various groups in the community. The displaced cottage weaver and the new factory loom fixer, or the independent cobbler and the shoe factory owner, saw the process differently. In part, the character of technological change has varied from period to period, and the effects in a period of high employment are likely to arouse reactions different from those in periods of already severe unemployment. Further, these diverse responses have been associated with different analyses of the ultimate effects of technological change and different valuations of stability or change, security or progress, and individual or social costs and benefits.

The current discussion over the severity of technological unemployment and the social consequences of automation must be placed in the perspective of the historical debate over the consequences of mechanization and technological change. Computers and transfer machines are new, but many of the issues they raise are old. The chapter by Robert Heilbroner provides the current discussion with historical perspective and identifies some of the questions regarding the economic and social consequences of technological change: What are the effects on employment? Does it improve or reduce living standards? Does it favor profits or wages? How does it affect the personality of the individual worker at the work place and at home, and what does it do to the larger society?

Technological change has been the underlying factor creating social changes in society. Lee DuBridge sketches in broad strokes some of the major areas of these social effects to date and still others that are in prospect. No social or political revolution in itself could possibly have wrought the consequences or the benefits to society that have been derived from technological change. These changes inevitably create some problems; automobiles bring problems of air pollution, and airplanes involve questions of air traffic control. But we are fortunate to have these problems rather than the issues of poverty, disease and hunger which characterize societies of low-level technologies. Mr. DuBridge also discusses technological change in relation to the educational system.

Floyd Mann summarizes the present state of our knowledge regarding the impact of automation in plants and offices upon individual workers and the work community. What are the consequences for job satisfaction, skill levels, training requirements, opportunities for promotion, relations to other workers and supervision? How do workers respond to automation at the work place and in their lives outside the work place? These questions have aroused widespread fears. It is imperative to provide dispassionate and detailed answers.

Automation has an impact not only upon the factory and plant employees, but also upon the managerial organization and upon managers. The nature of these effects is the subject matter of the chapter by Melvin Anshen. Does automation change the fundamental nature of management? What managerial functions does it most impinge upon? Does it lead to more or less centralization, and with respect to what aspects of managerial decision-making? Are its effects likely to be different at the levels of middle management or top management? Automation may be expected to have effects not merely on the managerial structure of business organizations but also upon governmental agencies, voluntary associations and various non-profit organizations.

One of the central areas of the impact of technological change and automation is collective bargaining. The relation is one of mutual interaction. Collective bargaining affects the rate of technological change, and technological change also constitutes an increasingly significant subject in a variety of ways for the parties to collective bargaining and to the government as it seeks to influence the environment of the parties. Does collective bargaining enhance or retard technological change? How does it balance personal and social costs against the gains of technological change? How does it reconcile the interests, which may not be identical, of the management, the workers, and the union in technological change? What price are we willing to pay for efficiency? How can the institutions of collective bargaining be better adapted to meet these problems in the public interest? George Taylor considers these fundamental questions.

Technological changes can no longer be regarded as exogenous to the economy, for changes in wages and prices affect the rate of technological change, and research and innovation are areas of business investment. W. Allen Wallis considers some of the more narrowly economic aspects of technological change.[1] May technological change be too rapid as well as too slow? What adjustments are required in wages and prices to facilitate adjustments to technological change? What economic policies determine the direction and character of technological change?

The impact of automation and technological change on employment or unemployment has attracted great attention. On the theoretical level, it has been argued that technological change results in no unemployment in the long run, and it has been contended with equal force that unemployment created by the technological change may persist for long periods. That there are initial displacement effects on employment from some technological changes cannot be denied. This range of issues is in desperate need of careful statistical work. Ewan Clague and Leon Greenberg make a contribution to this discussion by providing some estimates of the extent of some of the effects of technological change on employment in the postwar period. The chapter seeks to place the contribution of technological change to unemployment in quantitative perspective.

Technological change and automation may be expected to have a significant effect upon the international economic position of the United States. The rate of change is one factor influencing the level of prices and costs in the United States. The rates of change abroad, including the adoption in Western Europe and Japan of the latest technology, is a major factor influencing costs and prices in these countries, as well as their export position. What is our present relative position compared to that of other major industrial countries as to prices, wages and productivities? What is likely to be the impact of further technological change upon our relative position? Richard Cooper considers these decisive issues.

These chapters do not provide answers to all the questions that may be raised regarding the impact of technological change and automation. Nor do they provide an entirely consistent position on a number of vital questions. Indeed, the various authors from their diverse backgrounds, professional training and social philosophy, see the process of technological change in somewhat different terms, and at times they emphasize different consequences. But these different perspectives should contribute to a more stimulating construction and exchange of ideas.

[1] For a related discussion see, *Wages, Prices, Profits and Productivity*, The American Assembly, Columbia University, June, 1959, Charles A. Myers, ed.

Robert L. Heilbroner

1

The Impact of Technology:
The Historic Debate

In an age when it is possible to write seriously about a Death-of-the-World machine, it is hardly necessary to waste words on the power of technology to affect society. The shoe is now on the other foot: the brooding question is no longer what technology will make of man, but what man can still accomplish in the face of his technology. And it is not merely the apocalyptic potential of nuclear warfare which thus tilts the scales. At least in the Western world, where the typical landscape is industrial, where human life is sustained by the ceaseless operation of an enormous technical apparatus, where mechanical contrivances have penetrated into the smallest interstices of private life, it is not mere rhetoric to ask if Things are not already in the saddle, riding Man.

This extraordinary predominance of technology is the decisive characteristic of modern times. The political and ideological agonies of our age are not without parallels in the past. What gives them their "modern" character, what distorts their historic comparability, is above all the technological attributes of the situation to which they now apply. The conduct of peace as well as war, the most routine flow of the economic process, even the intimate details of social existence must cope, at every instant, with the magnifying presence of a gigantic and dynamic technological foundation for contemporary life.

And what is perhaps more chastening is the realization that we are

ROBERT L. HEILBRONER *is known for his books and articles on economic problems. In addition to* The Worldly Philosophers *and* The Future as History, *Mr. Heilbroner has written brochures for the World Bank, the European Community, and UNICEF, and has lectured on economic issues to university, foundation, business and labor groups. His latest book, published by Prentice-Hall, Inc., is* The Making of Economic Society.

still only entering upon this age of technological predominance. Science—
the moving force behind technology—is only now emerging from its in-
fancy: it has been said that of all the scientists of whom civilization has
any knowledge, 90 percent are alive today. And industrial technology—
the practical handmaiden of science—is equally new: half of all the research and development expenditures in the history of the United States
have been made in the last ten years. Hence the curve of the technological revolution continues to rise nearly vertically beneath our feet. With
each year its impact—on work and play, on mind and body—becomes
more unmistakable, more inescapable.

What will be the ultimate impact of this profound and cumulative
change in the shape of our environment? To what extent will technology
re-order society as it re-orders nature; to what extent will the machine
civilization of tomorrow liberate its creators—or impose upon them a
mechanical jig? If the specific focus of inquiry is on matters of economic
concern, the wider issues are readily visible in the background.

But our purpose in this introductory chapter will not be to plunge
into the ultimate issues themselves. It will be, rather, to establish a perspective from which to judge contemporary efforts to comprehend and
control our technological civilization. For the concern with technology
is not new. A long history of debate, both on its narrower economic aspects and on its broader social and philosophic influence, provides a
background against which our contemporary investigations may be
viewed, and indeed, without which they cannot be fully understood.
Hence it is a review of the historic debate that must first command our
attention. What have the economists, the sociologists, the philosophers
of the past 200 years to say about the revolution which already in their
day was irreversibly altering the condition of human existence?

THE ECONOMIC ISSUES

Adam Smith: the debate opens

It is worth our while to note at the outset why we begin a consideration
of the debate only 200 years ago, when clearly the impact of technology
is traceable infinitely further back. The reason is not far to seek. Whereas
the capacity of technology to alter the possibilities of life was clearly
visible to a Leonardo or a Bacon—not to mention an Archimedes—it
would be premature to describe their interest in machinery as "economic." Until a separate economic sphere of life had become visible
within the larger social matrix, until employment, incomes, and output,
for example, had become the unsettled variables of the social process,

the impact of technology was necessarily restricted rather than general.

Thus it is not surprising that technology enters the debate in virtually the same breath as that which presents us with our first comprehensive insights into the operation of nascent capitalism itself. In his epochal *Wealth of Nations,* Adam Smith sets the stage for an integration of technological change and economic growth.

The role of technology is not, however, immediately apparent. What, asks Smith, is the fundamental principle which underlies the disparities among the wealth of nations? His answer is the *division of labor,* as a consequence of which some nations achieve "the great multiplication of the productions of all the different arts . . . which occasions, in a well-governed society, that universal opulence which extends to the lowest ranks of the people."

But what in turn determines the degree to which labor can be divided and specialized? To Smith this *primum mobile* is "the extent of the market"—that is, the number of the population which possesses "the power of exchanging." And here is where technology makes its vital contribution. For Smith conceives of technical improvement and advance as a means of extending the market, not only by cheapening goods, but by augmenting the demand for labor itself: "The number of workmen in every branch of business generally increases with the division of labor in that branch, or rather it is the increase in their number which enables them to class and subdivide themselves in this manner." In other words, the growing market makes possible the introduction of a labor-specializing technology, and this technology, by *attracting* labor, in turn helps the market to grow. And to give yet another impetus to this reciprocal mechanism, "as the operations of each workman are gradually reduced to a greater degree of simplicity, a variety of *new* machines come to be invented for facilitating and abridging these operations."

Thus technological advance is not only conceived as a basic source of economic progress, but one which is continually refreshed and replenished by the consequences of progress itself. As both cause and effect of economic growth, a dynamic conception of technology was located by Smith at the very core of the economic process; and the *economic* repercussions of technological change were demonstrated to be wholly salutary.

Ricardo and Mill: the other side of the debate

Smith's sanguine appraisal of technological change was widely shared by most elements of English society in the early days of the Industrial Revolution. Only the working classes showed a stubborn incapacity to appreciate the benefits presumably accruing to them from the mills and factories springing up throughout the countryside. Loosely organized into bands said to be led by a "King Ludd," the Luddites burned and smashed the equipment for which, according to Adam Smith, they should have been grateful.

It is likely that their protest was more social than economic. The prisonlike aspect of the early mills repelled the agricultural proletariat, while the enforced regularization of work aroused what Andrew Ure, a Victorian spokesman, called "the refractory tempers of work-people accustomed to irregular paroxysms of diligence." Yet behind the social protest there lurked the germ of an economic doubt. The doubt did not concern the ability of technology to increase the output of goods for a given quantum of human effort. Rather, it asked whether, by virtue of that very increase, human effort would not become redundant. Centuries before, the emperor Vespasian had rejected the design for a hoisting machine, saying: "I must feed my poor." In similar fashion, a few early 19th century dissenters such as John Barton, raised the question as to whether the increasing demand for machinery might not actually decrease the demand for labor.

David Ricardo, the outstanding economist of the times, had at first shared the prevailing optimistic view of technology. He had, in fact, argued so persuasively against a fellow-economist, McCulloch, when the latter approved of Barton's views, that McCulloch had changed his mind. Now suddenly, in the 3rd edition of his famous *Principles,* published in 1821, Ricardo himself executed a startling turn-about. In a newly-inserted chapter *On Machinery* appeared the unexpected declaration that " . . . the opinion expressed by the labouring class, that the employment of machinery is frequently detrimental to their interests, is not founded on prejudice and error, but is conformable to the correct principles of political economy."

Ricardo's argument, to which McCulloch understandably took considerable exception, was a complicated one. Essentially it hinged on the premise that the demand for labor was determined by a *fixed* fund out of which capitalists paid the wages of labor. That is, each year a capitalist "advanced" wages to his workmen, who thereupon labored to produce commodities which the capitalist would eventually sell to recoup his wage outlays and to gain a profit. But now, says Ricardo, suppose a capitalist uses some of his wage-advances to have his workmen build him a machine. At the end of the year the capital invested in the machine will not be recouped, because the machine will not be sold, but will be used for next year's manufacture. During that next year the capitalist may very well make more profits, because of his new machine. But at the same time he will have less capital available from which to make further wage advances. Hence his capacity for employing workmen will fall.

Ricardo did not deny—and the point is an important one—that this increase in the capitalists' earning might not initiate a general expansion of trade. Neither did he deny that the dismissed workmen might not be reemployed if capitalists spent their enhanced revenues on menials (somewhat like the "transfer payments" of a welfare state). His argument rather was that this process of reemployment was a second and *entirely separate* step from the original substitution of machinery for labor. What was lacking was an automatic mechanism of compensation set into motion by the process of substitution itself.

Not only McCulloch, but most of Ricardo's followers, were dismayed at this conclusion. They might have hit back by challenging the strait-jacket premise of a fixed wage-fund, but instead they chose another avenue of attack. Ricardo, they said, had forgotten Say's Law: that the supply of a commodity creates its own demand (or as we would say, that costs and incomes are but opposite sides of the same coin). If technical progress lowered wages, it thereby either reduced costs or swelled profits. In either event real purchasing power would be increased, and as a result the demand for labor would receive a compensatory stimulus.

But would it? It was John Stuart Mill who pointed to a missing link in the argument of the "increased purchasing power" school. The increased demand for commodities, he said, need not be increased demand for labor. To be sure, the shift in income consequent upon a technological improvement augmented the real purchasing power of those *who were still engaged in the economic process*. But this was counterbalanced by the loss of purchasing power of those who had been displaced by the mechanical abridgment of labor. To put it differently, Mill admitted that Say's Law obtained in the sphere of production, but he denied that it was matched in the sphere of employment. An unchanged monetary flow—even an increase in aggregate real demand—might nonetheless be associated with diminished aggregate employment. Thus while technological change benefitted those who held on to their jobs, it promised no automatic benefits to those who did not.[1]

Karl Marx: technology and underconsumption

Yet, as with Ricardo, Mill could not be said to view technology pessimistically. At worst, the problem seemed to concern nothing more than a hitch in the market mechanism—an obstacle in the way of a smooth frictionless adjustment. Even more than Ricardo, Mill would have acquiesced in the contention of the optimists—that in the long run, the progressive introduction of machinery, by creating new industries and by cheapening costs, acted as a spur to economic development, and by implication, to social cohesion and contentment.

It was against this general consensus that Karl Marx launched his

[1] For this point, among others, I am indebted to Dr. Adolph Lowe. See his "Technical Unemployment Reexamined," *Wirtshaft und Kultursystem.* Zurich & Stuttgart, 1955.

powerful—albeit slow-acting—theoretical dissent. Here, for the first time, the long-run effects of technology were viewed as disruptive for the system as a whole.

The Marxian analysis begins, as does that of Smith and Ricardo, with an emphasis on capital accumulation, not only as the core of economic growth, but also as the potential agent of its undoing. Like Smith and Ricardo, Marx saw that the increasing demand for labor, stemming from expansion, would raise wages, lower profits, and thereby tend to bring the spiral of accumulation and growth to a halt. Smith and Ricardo had wriggled their way out of this *cul-de-sac* by recourse to a "law of population" which undercut the rising wages of factory hands by the rising numbers of factory offspring. But Marx had a more cunning and subtle mechanism of "escape." He proposed that the reserve army of the unemployed that is needed to hold down wages would be recruited, not from a climbing birth rate, but from labor continuously displaced by technological improvement. Thus in the Marxian schema technology played the crucial role formerly assigned to biology. It was the factor which, by relieving the pressure on wages, permitted the boom to go on.

But this was only the beginning of the analysis. For if, in the first instance, the introduction of machinery rescued the profit system, in the second instance it sounded its doom.

The demonstration follows logically enough from the Marxian system of assumptions. In the pure theoretical capitalism of Marxian theory, profit arises only from one source: the exploitation of human labor. That is, in the long run profit can never be wrung from machinery since the capitalist presumably pays full value when he purchases a machine in the first place, or as we would say, already discounts all its returns in the purchase price.

From these assumptions the Marxian analysis proceeds in its characteristic inexorability. (1) Capitalists, pitted against one another in a competitive struggle, are forced to introduce cost-cutting (labor-saving) machinery. Note that this integrates the process of innovation into the process of production, making the quest for technological superiority an inherent feature of capitalist competition. (2) As capitalists introduce technological change, they substitute machinery for labor, or in the Marxian terminology, constant capital for variable capital. Consequently, once the transient profits of innovation have been competed away, all capitalists are left with a higher "organic composition" of capital: that is, with less labor input per unit of output than before. (3) Since profit springs exclusively from labor, the *rate* of profit must therefore fall *pari passu* with the proportionate decline in labor input.

But worse follows. Thus far, technology has temporarily stimulated the accumulation process, only to depress it still more profoundly. Now technology brings the process to a total halt. For a basic assumption of

Marx is that the employment of labor has as a prerequisite the existence of employment-giving capital. In other words, jobs depend on the presence of equipment, such as lathes or looms or whatever. Hence to employ the technologically displaced labor force, more equipment must be provided. But how, asks Marx, are capitalists to become persuaded to produce more equipment in the face of the sagging consumption brought about by the displacement of labor? Thus, far from stimulating long-run expansion, technology brings the system to the crisis of an underconsumption collapse.

The marginalists: a counterattack

In one form or another the underconsumption argument has never quite ceased to bedevil the economist. But at least in the manner in which it is advanced by Marx, the argument hinges on a tacit assumption to which we have just paid heed: i.e. that it takes a certain fixed amount of capital equipment to give employment to a worker, or in the language of a contemporary economist, that the technical coefficients of production are fixed. In other words, to Marx there is only as much employment available as the stock of equipment (constant capital) offers, and any surplus of workers will more or less literally go begging for work.

By the late 19th century, however, another approach to the question of employment determination was advanced by the neoclassical economists, typified in our country by the work of J. B. Clark. Briefly, this school held that the wage of labor (as indeed of all the factors of production) was determined by the marginal contribution which it made to the value of output—that is, by its marginal productivity. Therefore, if there was a technological advance this meant only that new marginal productivities had been established, and that the ratios in which it was profitable to combine men and machines would have to be altered accordingly. But this was no reason, argued the marginalists, why unemployment should ensue. For at some lower wage, it would again be profitable for the employer to use labor instead of machinery, and at that wage all would find work.

If the marginalists were correct, then long-term technological unemployment on the Marxian model was indeed an impossibility. But were they right? In large part, the answer depends on the shape of the productivity curve—that is, on the actual changes in output associated with varying the input of labor applied to a fixed capital stock. For certain kinds of capital equipment—let us say for a fishing boat—the addition of extra hands will clearly be practicable and profitable as wages fall. But with other kinds of equipment—as for instance a modern high-speed printing press—the addition of extra hands *at any wage* will not significantly increase output. So long as one is not going to abandon the massive printing press itself, the number of working places it offers is strictly limited.

Hence the validity of the marginalists' argument must be judged against the specific nature of the technological apparatus itself. Whatever the adjustment possibilities for the long run, at least in the short run, when that apparatus is "given," the question appears not so much a theoretical problem as an empirical one.

Technocracy: the economics of depression

If the reader gains the impression, as we follow the course of the economic debate thus far, that the controversy was essentially an academic one, he would be entirely right. While there was always an underground of doubt about the machine, "respectable" popular opposition to the advances of technology had died with the Luddites. From the mid-19th century on, the man in the street inveighed not against technology, but against The Trusts—although had he stopped to think about it, he might have sensed a technological cause behind the process of trustification as well.

Suddenly, however, the underground of doubt burst into the open. With the advent of the Great Depression a new "school" of economic thought rose to overnight prominence. This was Technocracy, a word which temporarily at least seized the public imagination as had few economic terms of the past.

Purportedly stemming from Veblen's reflections on the machine (of which more later), technocracy relied for its appeal on the fact that it put boldly into the foreground the predominance of the machine in economic life. Writers in the Technocratic movement, such as Howard Scott or Stuart Chase, generally began their expositions with awed recitals of the power of the machine, both as a source of concentrated energy and as the labor equivalent of a growing number of men. For example, in words which have an ominously contemporary ring, Stuart Chase, in *Technocracy, an Interpretation,* voiced his concern over "the automatic factory (where the machine does *all* the physical work)," over the Buick assembly line where, between 1912 and 1927, production had risen 1400 percent and the labor force only 10 percent, or over the fact that two men with a power gang saw could "by pressing a button" produce between them in a day enough lumber to construct four 6-room houses.

What followed thereafter, however, was hardly conducive to a thoughtful discussion of the problem. "All philosophic approaches to social phenomena, from Plato to—and including—Marx, must be functionally avoided," wrote Howard Scott in *Introduction to Technocracy.* "Economics, that pathology of debt, not containing within itself any modulus or calculus of design or operation, must likewise be discarded with the other historical antiquities. . . ."

The characterization of economics as a "pathology of debt" is enlightening. For in fact, the Technocrats, after their obeisance to the engineering nature of the social process, eventually brought their positive proposals to the cluttered shrine of *monetary* reform. The technocratic movement blamed the machine for our ills, and then prescribed for the antidote a monetary unit based on an invariant standard of value, the erg. The effect was not a little like suggesting that an ill-organized factory could be put to rights by going on the metric system.

Technology and economic growth

Technocracy passed, leaving little imprint on academic thought. But the crushing problem of depression nonetheless refocussed professional attention on the problem of technology from an unexpected angle. It was no longer the quiet erosion of technological job displacement which now attracted the primary interest of investigators. Rather, it was the question with which Adam Smith himself had been originally concerned —that is, the role of technology in widening the market and thus promoting capitalist growth.

Already during the 1920's, a growing number of writers, including Bouniatian in France, Spiethoff and Schumpeter in Germany, Robertson in England, had stressed the "real"—as opposed to the "monetary"— causes of the business cycle, laying special emphasis on the discontinuous nature of the capital-building process. To these writers booms were the result of the opening of investment "opportunities," among which invention and technological change ranked high. To Josef Schumpeter, for instance, the entire trajectory of capitalist development was essentially set into motion by the fruitful combination of pioneering entrepreneurs and technological innovations, and this Schumpeterian theory of the business cycle rapidly gained considerable adherence during the 1920's.

Hence, as the Depression deepened, the question presented itself as to whether it might not be a dearth of these investment outlets—again including those of a technological nature—which lay at the heart of the trouble. In 1938 Alvin Hansen wrote, in *Full Employment or Stagnation*:

It is not true, as is sometimes alleged, that technological conditions have been uniformly and at all times equally favorable for new investment outlets. Not every period can be characterized as a kind of new industrial revolution. . . . It is true that in the course of time technology gave birth to the electrical and automobile age and with it to a new era of highway construction. Altogether these developments swallowed up vast sums of capital; but it is not difficult to see that this latter episode is nearing completion and, as has happened before, nothing else of equal magnitude has so far appeared above the horizon.

Hansen's rather tentative suggestion—it was no more than that—was quickly challenged, by (among others) Schumpeter himself. Briefly a controversy raged over the adequacy of investment outlets, particularly those of a technological nature. But in a sense the debate was an exercise in futility. For within three years of the publication of Hansen's book, the Second World War burst upon the American scene, bringing with it a total alteration of the institutional setting within which Hansen had written. With the rush of war investment came not only an unparalleled economic boom, but a hitherto unimagined—and indeed, unimaginable—horizon of technological advance.

On the momentum of this scientific floodtide we have ridden down to the present day. The doubts concerning the adequacy of technological opportunities have been stilled. But now, curiously, we find ourselves confronting an old issue in new guise. For as the problems of automation rise to engage our attention, we re-enter the debate, so to speak, at the stage of the 1830's. Today, once again, we must concern ourselves not with the volume of *investment* inherent in technological advance, but with the volume of *employment* which a technologically dynamic economy can offer.

THE SOCIAL ISSUES

If we were to halt now in our summary of the evolving views on the impact of technology, it is clear that our account would be seriously inadequate. For we have heretofore touched on the debate only insofar as it concerned the relationship of technology to employment and output. But if anything is certain, it is that technology does not limit its impact to these economic aspects of society. Far more profound, and in the long run, far more disarranging is its impact on the social habitat itself. In the terrible increase in the destructiveness of war, in the accelerating speed of travel and the weaving of networks of communication, in the complexity and size of social institutions, in the collectivization of modern life we sense the true end product of the machine. If we liken the incursion of technology to the dropping of a stone into a pool of water, we might say that its economic disturbances are but the initial splash, whereas the social alterations are the final and permanent displacement of water after the stone has sunk.

In one respect, however, the metaphor is misleading. For, unlike the case with a stone, when we consider the impact of technology it is the economic splash effect which is amenable to quantified and precise analysis, while the displacement effect—so easy to detect in the physical instance—is, in its social counterpart, amorphous and elusive and resistant to measurement. Hence when we turn to the debate over the social effects of technology we do not encounter a successive refining of insight, but rather a collection of *apercus,* of often persuasively but rarely logically formulated arguments, all of which exist more or less independently of each other. In the circumstances it would be fruitless to attempt a chronological review, parallel to the economic debate. Instead let us attempt to sift out two main themes which have interested social observers, and to suggest the variety of views which can be discovered among these observers. These two themes are: *What does the machine "do" to the man who attends it?,* and *What does the progressive addition of machinery "do" to the institutions of society which contain it?*

Impact on the worker

It is curious that the tone of the social debate, which we shall discover to be largely negative, is set by the same person to whom we owe the first vigorous affirmative verdict on the economic aspects of technology. In a famous passage of the *Wealth of Nations,* Adam Smith expressed a profound concern about the impact of machinery—otherwise so useful to society—upon those who came into immediate contact with it:

> . . . the understandings of the greater part of men are necessarily formed by their ordinary employments. The man whose whole life is spent in performing a few simple operations, of which the effects too are, perhaps, always the same, or very nearly the same, has no occasion to exert his understanding, or to exercise his invention in finding out expedients for removing difficulties which never occur. He naturally loses, therefore, the habit of such exertion, and generally becomes as stupid and ignorant as it is possible for a human creature to become. The torpor of his mind renders him, not only incapable of relishing or bearing a part in any rational conversation, but of conceiving any generous, noble, or tender sentiment. . . . His dexterity at his own particular trade seems, in this manner, to be acquired at the expense of his intellectual, social, [and] martial virtues.

We can trace a long line of thought which reflects, in part or whole, these misgivings. Sociologists and economists alike—not to mention artists and philosophers—have joined in deploring the decline in the creativity of work before the enforced rhythms and crushing routine of the machine process. Marx as usual is eloquent on this score as he describes the "individual insignificant factory operative . . . before the science, the gigantic physical forces, and the mass of labour that are embodied in the factory mechanism," and he sums up this impotence and estrangement of the worker in the concept of *alienation*. The theme has since been much explored in industrial sociology. Thus Walker and Guest in their well-known study of *The Man on the Assembly Line* conclude: "We suggest that the sense of becoming *de*-personalized, of becoming anonymous as against remaining one's self, is, for those who feel it, a psychologically more disturbing result of the work environment than either the boredom or the tension that arises from mechanically paced work."

Is there no dissent from this general unease concerning the human impact of technology? One general response comes quickly to mind. This is the reply that technology can also be a force which liberates men from "dehumanizing" toil—that is, a force which opens vistas of leisure time and which brings new and challenging work-demands into a life experience which was formerly only brutal and coarse. If we compare the spectacle of human exhaustion in a technologically primitive society with the relative ease and variety of human effort in an advanced society, there can be little doubt but that technology has operated as a large-scale agent of social amelioration over the long time-scale of history.

Yet it is instructive to note that this secular ameliorative aspect of technical change is not the aspect which has commanded the main focus of critical sociological or philosophic attention. As we survey the general literature, there is little doubt but that enthusiasts for the machine, *insofar as it bears on the human operative*, are few.[2] The problem which absorbs the social observer is not the historic liberation which technology has brought, but the immediate pressures which it imposes on those harnessed to its compulsive, repetitive processes.

But cannot these processes be softened, and the mechanical impact on the operative cushioned by more enlightened practices? We might listen in this regard to the sociologist Durkheim:

> As a remedy, it has sometimes been proposed that, in addition to their technical and special instruction, workers be given a general education . . . . No doubt, it is good for the worker to be interested in art, literature, etc., but it is nonetheless bad that he should be treated as a machine all day long. Who cannot see, moreover, that two such existences are too opposed to be reconciled, and cannot be led by the same man! If a person has grown accustomed to vast horizons, total views, broad generalities, he cannot be confined, without impatience, within the strict limits of a special task . . . .

Yet unexpectedly, it is from Durkheim that we also get another side of the case for technology. For in his view, the process of the division and

---

[2] An unusual exception is Alfred Marshall who describes a delicate screwmaking machine and suggests that "the person who minds it must have an intelligence and an energetic sense of responsibility, which go a long way toward making a fine character." But he hastens to add, "No doubt this is an extreme case." (*Principles* 1948 ed., N. Y. p. 258).

specialization of labor, far from necessarily obliterating the human personality, in fact offers it its only avenue for expression. In an advanced society, says Durkheim, man can no longer hope to extend his competence over the entire range of social activity. He must become an organ of society, and in the expert discharge of his constricted but useful task, he will find the most meaningful bond to his fellow men. Hence the remedy is not to abandon specialization. It is to flesh it out with meaning, to give the worker the ability to see his small task as part of a larger whole.

It must be admitted that Durkheim is far from clear as to how this integration of task and meaning is to take place. But at least he brings to our attention two critical points. The first is that the "impact" of technology cannot be considered as residing merely in the machine, but in the *social uses* of the machine. And the second is that industrial technology has at least a potential function in providing social solidarity. Thus Durkheim widens the screen from an exclusive focus on the individual engaged in the industrial process to the interaction of all persons in industrial society. In a word, he broadens the discussion from the impact of technology upon the worker to its impact upon the social whole.

The civilization of the machine

Can one make some meaningful appraisal of this ultimate social effect of technology? Once again we encounter the general argument of those who stress the economic gains from technology, in particular the immense increase in individual material well-being. Yet, as in the case with the individual operative, the historic contentions of social philosophers have tended along a different line. Rather than stressing the social gain stemming from an increase in the quantity of life's goods, they have largely emphasized the social loss stemming from a putative deterioration in the quality of industrial life itself. Thus we find Jefferson's distrust of the urban-industrial life as inimical to the independence of the human spirit, or Spengler's cry that "Man has felt the machine to be devilish, and rightly," or Jasper's description of "the immense joylessness which technology brings into the world."

Such statements are powerful and, it may be, deeply important. Yet when we ask ourselves exactly in what way the quality of life is adversely affected by the incursion of the machine, we find that however powerful the outcry against technology, the complaints are largely metaphorical. They describe, often very compellingly, the *feelings* of the observer, but they are rarely if ever explicit in describing the causal process leading to the end product they deplore. Hence we may find it more interesting to examine two other main lines of approach which attempt in more systematic fashion to relate technology to society.

The first of these stresses the role of technology in altering—for better or worse—the degree of *rationality* which characterizes the social situation. Many observers have been fascinated by the possibilities for mental discipline inherent in a mechanized environment. Herbert Spencer, for example, established a grand dichotomy between military and industrial societies in his *Principles of Sociology* and was bold enough to predict the gradual supremacy of the rational, anti-authoritarian patterns of thought on which he believed an industrial order to be based. Perhaps better known is Thorstein Veblen's elaboration of essentially the same view. To Veblen the mechanical compulsions of the industrial work-process brought a change in the world-view of the industrial participant. "The machine," he wrote, in *The Theory of Business Enterprise*, "throws out anthropomorphic habits of thought. . . . It inculcates think-ing in terms of opaque, impersonal cause and effect. . . . "Thus," he concluded, "in the nature of the case the cultural growth dominated by the machine industry is of a skeptical, matter-of-fact complexion, materialistic, unmoral, unpatriotic, undevout."

This is not, however, the only assessment of the characterological im-pact of technology. To another group of observers, ironically enough, the technological process, with its incomprehensible complexities and recurrent malfunctions, is the source of a growing *irrationality* in human affairs. Durkheim himself, having posited the potential function of industrial specialization in promoting social cohesion, nonetheless warns how a disparity between social and technological organization can give rise to the *anomie* of a sick society. Similarly, Karl Mannheim writes: "Just as nature was unintelligible to primitive man, and his deepest feelings of anxiety rose from the incalculability of the forces of nature, so for modern industrialized man the incalculability of the forces at work in the social system under which he lives, with its economic crises, in-flation, and so on, has become a source of equally pervading fear."

Unhappily, then, the study of the impact of technology on social rationality seems to lead to inconclusive results. But there is yet a second general approach to the over-all effect of technology on the social system. This is the view of technology as the source of *institutional* change.

The archetype of this view is, of course, the materialist conception of history. "The ultimate causes of all social change and political revo-lutions," writes Engels in an oft-quoted passage from Anti-Dunring, "are to be sought, not in the minds of men . . . but in changes in the mode of production and exchange . . . ;" or as Marx himself wrote: "Social relations are closely bound up with productive forces. In acquiring new productive forces men change their mode of production; and in changing their mode of production they change their ways of earning a living— they change all their social relations. The handmill gives you society with the feudal lord; the steam-mill society with the industrial capitalist."

Of all the Marxian pronouncements this may be the most penetrative, and to some degree the economic "interpretation" of history colors all our views of the past. But it is, alas, a less illuminating insight when we turn to the future. It may be that the handmill "gave" us society with the feudal lord and the steam-mill society with the industrial capitalist. Do the computer and the atom then give us society with the commissar? We cannot truthfully answer the question, in the affirmative or negative. The exact manner in which technology and the mode of production "impose" their will on the political and social superstructure is but little understood, if indeed, at all. However brilliant as a general retrospective insight, the Marxian interpretation of history is not yet a precise tool of scientific prediction.

THE RELEVANCE OF THE DEBATE

And thus a review of the debate—necessarily more fragmentary in the case of the social issues than the economic—brings us to the problems with which the succeeding essays in this volume will be concerned. But a recapitulation of the argument and counter-argument of the past serves a more useful purpose than merely guiding us to the present. It gives us as well a frame of reference from which we may draw a few issues pertinent to the contemporary prospect.

Limitations of traditional theory

One thing strikes us forcibly as we reflect on the course and content of the debate. This is the failure of theory as yet to cope adequately with the problems of the impact of technology.

The failure is, no doubt, most glaring in the case of the social theorists. What lacks here, it is clear enough, is not over-all vision or profound intuition, but systematic and scientific analysis—which is to say, the only kind of analysis which will allow vision and intuition to be translated into fruitful action. What is missing from the social theorists are the specific empirical findings, the hard facts and dispassionate comparisons without which their *obiter dicta* remain in the metaphorical rather than in the manipulable world.

When we reflect on the economic debate, however, just the opposite conclusion is forced upon us. Here is a mass of facts and findings, but all too rarely a central binding concept. Indeed, there is often lacking even a central concern. For in one respect the Technocrats were right: the steady invasion of technology *is* the commanding reality that shapes the economic relation of man to nature in our day. How extraordinary, then, that the two most important economists of fullblown capitalism, Alfred Marshall and Lord Keynes, have virtually nothing to say about the impact of technology on the economic system! Indeed, save for Marx —and to a much lesser degree Veblen and Schumpeter—we look in vain for an exposition in which technological change is organically incorporated as *both* a source of growth and disruption in economic evolution.

Clearly, what is needed today is a "unified" theory of technology— a theory which will bring together both the impetus and the undertow of technological progress as it affects the economic process. What still lacks is a conception of the technological process sufficiently broad to comprehend its long-range and its short-range impacts, alive to its secular re-arrangements of society as well as to its mixed creative and disruptive effects on the economy. The objective may well exceed our grasp. But it is certainly the direction of inquiry toward which a review of the historic debate urges us.

Changes

The Changing Social Matrix of Technology—But a review of the debate reveals not only the need for a more comprehensive approach to the impact of technology. Equally it clarifies for us some of the main avenues along which research must proceed if it is to remedy the shortcomings of the past.

One of these avenues concerns the changing social and institutional matrix of technological change. Implicit in the early theories of technological change was the assumption that invention and innovation were the products of a highly competitive environment: Marx, we will recall, introduced technology into his system as a direct consequence of competition. What has yet to be systematically investigated, however, is the manner in which the introduction of technology itself changes the nature of the institutional background whence it arises. As Galbraith has pointed out in *American Capitalism,* contemporary technical improvement is largely located not in the competitive but in the oligopolistic sectors. And beyond even that it seems increasingly evident that basic research has now grown too big even for the largest industrial organizations, and must originate in programs of government support. Hence, when we stress the rising curve of research and development today, we must not fail to include the radical change in the institutions and sponsorship under which technological change is brought into being.

This may have a social significance as well as an economic. For it means that to a growing degree the process of technological change is no longer the spontaneous product of market forces but the deliberate creation of public or quasi-public effort. Thus the problem of the *control* over the entry of technology becomes, at least on the surface, more amenable to public decision. Perhaps this slow drift towards the socialization of technological change opens the way for a new examination of social policy in the guidance of the technological revolution.

The Changing Nature of Technology—Closely associated with the problem of the evolving matrix of technical change is a second issue to which the historic debate also alerts us. This is the need to study the changing form of technology itself.

From our consideration of the controversy over the displacement effect of machinery, one aspect of this problem is immediately clear. As the marginalist counter-argument brought out, the shape of the labor productivity curve is all-important in determining the degree to which technological improvements "create" unemployment, at least in the short run. What we now need to investigate is whether this empirical problem has an *historical* aspect—whether, in other words, there is visible a progressive change in the employment-granting possibilities of successive stages of technical advance.

In an age of accelerating technological change this has obvious economic implications. But the changing nature of technology bears as well on the social implications of the future. Will, for instance, an increasing mechanization of industry bring to a still higher pitch the psychological "demasculinization" of work of which even the World Health Organization now speaks? Must we resign ourselves to the view of Norbert Wiener that "taking the Second [Industrial] Revolution as accomplished, the average human being of mediocre attainments or less [will have] nothing to sell that is worth anybody's money to buy?" Or will automation, by effecting a shift from manufacturing into service occupations, indirectly make possible again more of a face-to-face, personalized work experience? These questions, of great social and economic import, await for an answer a far deeper comprehension of the "laws" of technological change than we now possess.

The Changing Social Adjustment to Technology—A third crucial question also emerges from our historical retrospective. This is the nature of our secular adjustment to the productive power of industrial technology.

In part, of course, this is a familiar economic question. As Gerard Piel has pointed out: "One man-hour of work today produces what it took three man-hours to produce sixty years ago. This means that we could be producing the same national product as in 1900 with one-third of the 1900 labor force. That would leave 58 million members of the present labor force unemployed."

The fact that we do not have 58 million unemployed is traceable to three factors. First, we produce a much larger product than we did in 1900. Second, we work many fewer hours per person, and thereby trade productivity for leisure. And third, we have shifted the work force away from the goods-producing sector into the service sector: we have followed Ricardo's advice and increased our employment of menials.

But it is one thing to identify the means by which we have adjusted to the onslaught of technology and another to relate these means to one another and to the over-all process in some systematic fashion. Is there a relationship between these crucial variables of adjustment? What are the social mechanisms by which technological advance on the grand scale is translated into employment, into leisure, and into a new distribution of productive effort?

Once again, however, there is here a larger problem than that of economics alone. For in its widest implications the problem of secular "adjustment" brings us again to a consideration of how the human personality and the social organism become acclimated to the new environment which technology creates for them.

And here we return again to the "positive" aspect of technology to which we have previously referred. Throughout the historic debate we have noted a continuing counterpoint of argument between those who, on the one hand, have emphasized the cramping, the stultifying, the "dehumanizing" aspect of technology, and those who have replied by stressing its basic gifts of wealth and leisure. If, as we have noted, there are few celebrants of the industrial process as a tonic for the human spirit, there have been many who have sought to justify its relentless advance in terms of the gradual limitation, even the elimination, of work itself. To them the machine offers the ultimate reward of an escape from the historic indenture of man to scarcity and toil.

But the question is: escape into what? It is no longer sheer fantasy to look ahead to the day when technology will present society with the gift of an immense wealth together with an equally immense vacuum of toil. How that wealth will then be used and how that vacuum filled; what sorts of activities, public or private, will then take the place of the eternal bondage of men to labor; what potentialities for creativity, waste, or destruction may then be unleashed—these are surely among the supreme questions for the future. Neither goods nor leisure are yet so abundant that an increase in both would not be called a boon by the great majority of men. Yet already one can ask if the disorders of contemporary society are not traceable in some degree to a superfluity of some kinds of wealth and to an inadequate opportunity to perform challenging work. The problem of social existence in a world crammed with goods and emptied of work is still in the future. But already we stand on its outermost threshold.

New directions for inquiry

These are some of the reflections which a review of the historic debate on the impact of technology bring to mind. They are reflections to which, unfortunately, we cannot as yet give an adequate response. Even the "simplest" of questions—the over-all impact of technology on employment and output—is still only uncertainly understood. Far less do we comprehend the effect of technology on "man," and still less again its enormous pressure on the moulding of society.

Insofar as this ignorance reflects the disparity between our crude instruments of social inquiry and the delicate refinement of the problems, our lack of understanding can only be ruefully accepted. Unfortunately, however, our ignorance is not merely the result of the obduracy of the issues. It is symptomatic as well of a failure to mount a bold intellectual assault upon the problem itself. Adrift on a furious current of technology, we allow ourselves to be swept along, trusting to the blind forces at work to bring us safely to some unknown but unquestioned destination. It need hardly be pointed out that this belief in the benign social impact of technology may turn out to have been the most tragic of all contemporary faiths. Hence, while there is still time left, we must peer courageously ahead, take audacious triangulations on our course, seek to combine empiricism and speculation on the grand scale. Perhaps now, as the perils and promise of technology seize our imaginations and crowd our awareness as never before, it may be possible to launch such an effort to understand and guide our fate. For in this age of technical virtuosity Man will surely never ride Things unless he is prepared to ask questions which today do not often seem to occur to him.

Lee A. DuBridge

2

Educational and Social Consequences

THE IMPACT AND CHALLENGE OF TECHNOLOGY

In the past one hundred years, advances in science and technology have produced revolutionary change in the Western world—change in the patterns of human living, and change in the social and political institutions which have been evolved to enable great numbers of people to live together on a planet which no longer seems very large. That these social and political institutions are, in many respects, inadequate to their task is only too painfully obvious.

Indeed, some have suggested that science and technology be halted for a while to allow human beings to invent a better society in which to live, one better adapted to the technological advances already made. Aside from the impossibility of forcing men to stop thinking, or preventing them from taking advantage, in a material sense, of the products of their thinking, it seems evident that this proposal represents a wholly inverted conception of what has happened in the last hundred years. It assumes that new knowledge and inventions are inherently "bad"—and that their evil effects can be alleviated and their impact cancelled only by inventing social or political devices.

The situation is quite the reverse. New discoveries in science and tech-

LEE A. DuBRIDGE, *president of The California Institute of Technology, has been a professor of physics (at Washington University), a dean of arts and science (at the University of Rochester), and a director of radar research (at M.I.T.). He is a member of The National Science Board, the National Academy of Science, and The American Philosophical Society, and a fellow of The American Physical Society. Dr. DuBridge is a board member of, among other organizations, the Rockefeller Foundation and the Mellon Institute.*

nology have solved or alleviated far more human and social problems than they have created. They have vastly reduced hunger and disease; they have (in the Western world, at least) largely lifted the burdens of hard manual labor, and thus made possible the abolition of slavery—including the worst forms of economic slavery formerly imposed on the working classes. Technological change has brought to foreseeable attainment the age-old ideal of human beings living, not in conditions of degrading deprivation, but in a high degree of physical comfort.

No purely social or political inventions could ever have achieved a revolution like this. Yet it is inevitable that when such a revolution is in process a social pattern built on prerevolutionary conditions will need radical alteration to take full advantage of changes. Technological change solves or alleviates old problems, but in the process sets up new conditions which challenge men to invent new social and political mechanisms to take full advantage of changes, and thus to seek a still better way of living. There are many examples of such challenges.

The advances in agricultural technology in the United States, together with advances in food transport and preservation, have virtually eliminated hunger—but have created a problem of how to deal with food and labor surpluses during a transition period when there are too many farmers.

The advances in medicine have created a problem of providing a better life for the many older people who, in past times, would long ago have died of disease.

Automobiles and trucks have become indispensable to us because they created a mobile nation. They eliminated the loneliness of the farmer's family, brought city dwellers to more spacious suburban areas, destroyed a large share of the provincialism of a vast nation. But they have also made a shambles of our efforts at city planning. With the airplane, they have brought our vaunted railroad system to a state of perpetual crisis. They kill and injure thousands of people each year. They have solved old problems—and created new ones.

Advancing industrial technology first created and then eliminated child labor and the sixty-hour week; created and subsequently abolished a host of industrial health hazards; brought a multiplicity of material comforts to every home, office, factory, and farm—but in recent years has left a residual unemployment problem that defies our best efforts to solve.

Resulting social problems

Yet the problem currently referred to as "automation" must be viewed against this much larger problem of technical change. For technical changes have been occurring in human civilization ever since the in-

vention of the wheel. Each such change—except possibly those relating
exclusively to the technology of warfare—has brought new opportunities,
new comforts, new possibilities for better, safer, and less painful living.
And it is no new thing that each has also brought new problems. Some
of these changes called for still further technical development—automobiles required better roads; airplanes forced the better processing of
aluminum and other materials; the Edison filament lamp created the
electric power industry, and so on. Other changes forced new government
activities and agencies—for example, the growth of huge transportation
and communication systems demanded government regulatory bodies, as
did the mass production of packaged foods and drugs. The United States
Departments of Health, Education, and Welfare, of Agriculture, of
Commerce, and of Labor deal substantially with problems arising from
technological changes. In addition, the growth of scientific knowledge—
and the benefits which follow—have become so important to national life
that many new government agencies have been created to accelerate
research and development in scientific and technical fields: the National
Institutes of Health, the National Science Foundation, the Atomic
Energy Commission, the National Aeronautics and Space Administration,
among others.

Social institutions, too, have changed as a result of technical innovation. The large corporation was required to raise the capital necessary
to build new industrial and business enterprises. The labor unions grew
up to meet abuses resulting from industrialization—and to help insure
that a substantial share of the fruits of increased productivity be returned to the workers. The growth of large cities—impossible without
transport, communication, and a myriad of industrial products—has
forced the development of a host of social institutions: welfare and relief
agencies, public health and hospital services, fire and police departments.
And these same cities have made possible the growth of cultural and
recreational organizations impossible in a rural society: art galleries,
musical and dramatic organizations, service and charitable clubs, and—
most important of all—a modern educational system.

In every case the new technical, governmental, or social changes
brought on by technological and scientific advances had a double
purpose: not only to avoid dangers and evils which these advances
brought in their wake, but also to preserve and improve and make more
available for public use the great advantages which the same advances
made possible.

And it is in this light that we should view the social problems raised
by technological change. Each such change, if it is widely adopted (and
therefore merits our attention), must have brought great advantages to
many people, and usually to society as a whole. But it may eventually
bring dangers too. Penicillin has been a boon to mankind—yet it makes
some people violently sick. Shall we then abolish penicillin—or find ways

to protect the unfortunate few? Shall we abolish automobiles to prevent accidents and air pollution—or find ways to alleviate these undesired and unpredictable consequences?

What Is Automation?

Automation is a new word, but not a new phenomenon. The cotton gin and the reaper-binder and the tractor brought automation—mechanization, if you prefer—to the farm, with attendant blessings and problems. The steam engine first mechanized industrial production—indeed, it made modern industrial production possible. Electric motors carried the process of mechanization much further—because of improved economy, convenience, speed, and safety (few people still recall the bewildering and hazardous maze of belts and pulleys, shafts and levers that completely filled the old steam-powered factories and shops). And when electronic devices began to provide automatic controls for the electric motors, the term *automation* crept in.

However, the development has been continuous ever since modern industrial processes were initiated in the late 18th and early 19th century. Steam power was first used to do the heavy, cumbersome jobs—pumping water, lifting coal from deep mines, operating large saws in a lumber mill, lifting and moving heavy loads in the iron works, operating the large looms in a textile mill, and so on.

With such power available, larger and more elaborate machine tools became possible—and were soon put in use. Huge lathes and presses and milling machines could now fabricate—often with high precision—huge metallic components for all sorts of uses: steel beams for factories and skyscrapers, boilers and drive-wheels for locomotives, heavy steel plates and enormous steam turbines for ships, steam-powered farm machinery —the list is endless.

Machines, however, were not adapted exclusively to heavy jobs. They took on light and delicate ones too—and achieved them at speeds never believed possible. Witness a modern cigarette machine which fills, cuts, and packages cigarettes so fast that the eye can scarcely follow. And one of the most astonishing of all industrial processes is the machine that automatically makes gas-filled electric lamp bulbs—accurately blows the glass, winds and mounts a delicate filament, evacuates the bulb, fills it to a predetermined pressure with a rare gas, seals, anneals, tests, mounts on a base, and ejects at a breathtaking speed. Such machines have been in use—with steady improvements, of course—since long before the word "automation" was invented.

Consider also the automatic telephone exchange. It was only forty years ago or so when experts were calculating that, at the rate telephones were being installed, it would be but a few years before every young woman in the United States were needed to operate the manual exchanges. (There would be no one left to *talk* on the telephones!) Think of how many potential jobs were eliminated by the automatic dial phone! But the telephone companies now employ more men and women, by far, than they did forty years ago.

What precisely, then, do we mean by *automation?* In reality it is simply a new name for the current stage of development of the old process of mechanization. And what characterizes the current stage? Normally, the word is used to describe the multiplicity of electronic devices now used to control industrial processes—to monitor the quality of the product and adjust the machine to correct for deviations, to compute in advance the rate at which materials and parts of particular types should be fed into a complex assembly line, and to continue the process of taking over more and more of the repetitious processes formerly done by hand—and performing them with a delicacy, precision, and speed that human hands could never match. The push-button factory is now nearly a reality; it *is* a reality in certain cases.

An important contribution to this automation process has been the development of the modern high-speed electronic computer and data-processing machine. Such machines have certain capacities that are almost human, such as remembering, learning from past experience, recalling and quickly using a multiplicity of facts and instructions.

They also have superhuman qualities—especially the ability to perform a million acts of addition (or subtraction) in *one second.* Such a machine renders obsolete the old processes of bookkeeping, auditing, account-keeping, inventory control, payroll handling, and many other business and fiscal operations. It also makes a major contribution to the automatic industrial process. And it makes possible also a host of scientific, engineering, and technical calculations never before feasible. It has been said that the calculations of the orbits of the planets around the sun—on which Johannes Kepler worked laboriously for a lifetime—could now be completed in a few minutes. One can now compute quickly, in advance, the stresses, strains, and possible failures of a bridge, a building, or other structure when subjected to storms, floods, or earthquakes—and can rapidly incorporate the necessary corrective design features.

We think of an automobile assembly line as a device for turning out rapidly hundreds of identical cars each day. But the modern assembly line—with automation—can arrange things so such a line may operate for years and produce no two cars which are identical—each differing from all others in color combination, body style, accessory equipment, engine model, and other choices specified in advance.

In short, the process of electronic control and computation has added one more stage of refinement to the age-old process of relegating burdensome and repetitious manual and mental tasks to machines—machines of such multiplicity, variety, and complexity that a whole industry is devoted to making machines for other industries.

THE RISE IN PRODUCTIVITY

It is true that the introduction of electronic techniques into manufacturing processes has produced, in certain cases, some spectacular results—so much so that the term *automation* has come to suggest a complete revolution in industrial processes. Fears have thus been raised that the worker is soon to become obsolete and that very large unemployment problems will result. While there is some truth in this, the problem should not be exaggerated. A look at the history of the mechanization of industry shows in fact that the recent introduction of automation has produced no radical change in the trend.

The major indication of the effectiveness of improved technological changes in manufacturing is reflected in the figures for productivity per man-hour. As more products can be produced with a given amount of labor, the Gross National Product rises, even though, at the same time, the average work week may gradually decline. This is, of course, highly desirable.

The figures on the annual rate of change of productivity per man-hour have been given by John W. Kendrick in *Productivity Trends in the United States*. They show that during the ten-year period from 1909 to 1919 the annual rate of increase of productivity per man-hour was only .8 percent per year. From 1929 to 1937, the mechanization of industry proceeded on a much more rapid basis, and the average rate of change rose to 5.6 percent per year, partly a result of the depression which eliminated inefficient units. Between 1937 and 1948, however—this time affected by the war interruption—the rate of change dropped to 1.4 percent per year. In the spectacular change in industrial manufacturing processes that occurred between 1948 and 1953, the annual rate of change was still only 3 percent per year. The figures for the years since 1953 are not complete, but the indications are that the rate has continued at roughly 3 percent per year, which is about the average of the past fifty years. There are substantial fluctuations from year to year, but the general trend is continuous. If anything, we should worry that automation is not proceeding fast enough to keep production increases well ahead of the population increase.

Thus, the assertion that automation is producing a very spectacular rise in productivity, and thereby causing an unusually severe and widespread unemployment problem, is not borne out by the facts. The nature of the technological changes being introduced into industrial manu-facturing processing has altered, but the trend has been continuous.

Thus, in spite of spectacular improvements in productivity in certain individual processes, the over-all picture is not essentially different in recent years from that of the last forty years.

Results of increases in productivity

The net effect of the gradual increase in productivity means that with an approximately constant number of man-hours per year (the rising working population being nearly compensated by the decreasing number of hours worked per week), it has been possible to double the output of industrial production every twenty-five to thirty years while the popu-lation has been doubling every forty-five to fifty years. This, of course, is the primary source of the increased standard of living which this country has been attaining over the past century.

And the net result of all the improvements in productivity can be seen by looking about us. Compare the way of life of a typical citizen in any American city or small town with that enjoyed by his counterpart of one hundred years ago—or by his counterpart in any town of Europe five hundred years ago—or by his counterpart today in any village of India, Burma, Indonesia, or equatorial Africa. Those who object to, and resist, today's automation must logically reject yesterday's mechani-zation—and must then reject as undesirable and bad the whole of modern industrial development. They must advocate, in short, the re-turn to the most primitive forms of society of hundreds of years ago—a society which, by now, with inevitable population increases—would be choked and paralyzed by hunger, disease and poverty. No one advocates that.

Let us not complain, then, if a modern society poses some social problems which the older societies did not face. Starving men do not worry about the regulation of air traffic, telephone systems, railroads, or automobiles—or even about labor unions and big business. Nor do they worry about schools or colleges or churches or hospitals or symphony orchestras or art galleries or theaters. And, of course, they don't worry about fallout shelters and nuclear war. They always *have* worried about unemployment and even taxes.

It is not my intention to belittle the serious problems we do face; they are in many respects frustrating, terrifying, and in some respects seemingly insoluble. All I say is that we in the United States are lucky to have these problems substituted for the age-old problems of wide-spread starvation, poverty, and disease.

Present Problems

What, in essence, *are* the problems we face after a century or more of scientific and technological development. There are many. Let me name a few:

1. The avoidance of war.
2. The maintenance of a free society.
3. The spreading of the benefits of these technological advances to *all* people: to all classes in this country, eventually to the people of all nations.
4. The avoidance of suffering, distress, broken lives, and injustice which result from the adjustment to new conditions resulting from technical advance—e.g., unemployment, class and race discrimination, local disruption caused by changing industrial or agricultural patterns.
5. The regulation in the public interest of evils which result from the selfishness of those who manage the large and powerful agencies which modern society finds necessary—big business, big labor unions, and big government.
6. The evolution of new social, economic and political mechanisms which will achieve the above objectives—and which will also help bring about the realization of many new technological developments that are now impractical because of economic or social inadequacies—e.g., finer cities, pure air, abundant water and power, providing adequate food for hungry millions in Asia and Africa.
7. The creation of an educational system which will enable people everywhere to understand the changing world in which they live and better adapt themselves to it—and thus lead happier, more meaningful and more fruitful lives.

This is an imposing list of problems—and there are more. I could not begin adequately to discuss them all—or even any one of them—here. Let me make only some brief comments on the last two.

The social problems related to technical advance, as I have said, have a double aspect: first, to reduce the dangers and inequities resulting from past developments; and, second, to open the way for future advances. It is this positive endeavor that needs further emphasis. For when it is successful, it will often reduce the negative problems and also bring about new human benefits.

It may be interesting to reflect on the fact that scientific knowledge has already advanced far enough to provide technical answers to the following problems:

1. Elimination of man-made air pollution.
2. Reduction of metropolitan traffic congestion.

3. Supplying fresh water from the sea.
4. Further increases in agricultural production.
5. Energy production from uranium.
6. Great increase of industrial production through further improved technology.

There are many others. But these are samples of some of the most challenging—and the most difficult. In each of the five areas, an important barrier to faster progress is an economic one. Great as the individual benefits may be, the costs are often even greater. There are those who will express disgust and disbelief at such a situation. "Money must never be an obstacle to social advance," some say. But it *has* often been an obstacle—and often will be. If it costs $2000 per year to provide enough fresh water from the sea to irrigate a plot of ground that can only produce $500 worth of food, one has reached an economic impasse. It may be solved if technical developments reduce the cost—or if in some areas the values placed on the food produced are very much higher. But, in the great arid regions of this country—a nation already plagued by surplus food—the economic impasse is very real.

Pure air

If the cost of regaining pure air in a city is the elimination of all devices that burn coal or oil or gasoline or gas—again the cost is too high. In this case, further technical advances appear to be in sight—yet the cost of eliminating pollutants from auto exhausts is sure to be very great. Is it worth $100 per car to reduce the pollution level in Los Angeles to, say, half its present value? Who decides? And who bears the cost? It is not a simple *yes* or *no* question. One thing is certain—Los Angeles smog could be almost completely eliminated by prohibiting the driving of automobiles, buses, and trucks. Clearly, however, this would be far too costly and far too disruptive even to contemplate. Viewed in this light, we see that the problem of smog is only a fairly minor adverse effect of a technological development which has produced vast benefits.

Traffic

Another problem raised by the wide use of automotive vehicles concerns traffic congestion in metropolitan areas. Clearly, the problem here is primarily an economic one, though it has many political and social overtones. These traffic problems could be greatly relieved by the construction of large multiple-highway or freeway systems—some elevated or some underground—by the construction of large public parking facilities, and by the evolution of new mechanisms of mass transportation. All of these enterprises are technically feasible. The economic problem can be illustrated by imagining the cost of erecting an eight-lane freeway down through the middle of Manhattan, connected with a dozen or more crosstown freeways at suitably spaced intervals. The cost of such a project is obviously so colossal as to be rejected at first sight. No doubt other less expensive solutions could be developed, but economic factors would certainly be all but prohibitive in any case. Are we then going to be forced to live forever with the problem of traffic congestion? Or can new technical or economic solutions be developed? Here is a technical-economic-political problem far more challenging and sweeping in its potential than all of the problems posed by the field of automation.

Nuclear power

Another technically feasible operation is that of producing large amounts of electrical power with the use of uranium-fueled reactors. Many technical problems remain to be solved, particularly in the area of insuring safety of such installations in case of accident or disaster. But the primary problem is now an economic one. The cost of supplying large-scale power to the entire country by uranium reactors is still much greater than that of supplying it by more conventional means. And this will remain true until further technical developments occur in reactor technology, or until we begin exhaustion of our supply of fossil fuels. In any case, "cheap and abundant" power from uranium is still far in the future.

Accelerating productivity

Finally, of course—and more to the point—is the question not of how we can prevent the further mechanization and automation of industry, but of how we can accelerate its progress and attain a very much more rapidly rising manufacturing productivity. The technical means are at hand to improve vastly many industrial manufacturing processes. The barriers are: (1) technical problems of adapting present knowledge to new uses; (2) the large amounts of capital required; and (3) the social problems caused by a too-rapid displacement of workers. Nevertheless, as previously stated, it is this positive problem of bringing about much greater industrial productivity, and doing it without widespread suffering among the workers, which should challenge our attention and our efforts.

It should be recalled in this connection, however, that, of all the more than 70 million employed persons in the United States, only 16.5 million are engaged in manufacturing industries. Thus, if we could in any single year improve industrial productivity by the miraculous figure of 10 percent, 1.6 million workers would be displaced, assuming the total volume of manufactured products remained the same. But such a great expansion of productivity would create new industries, expand many old ones, produce cheaper products and an expanded market, so that the actual displacement would be far smaller. Surely, then, if we set a more modest goal of increasing our productivity from the present rate of increase of 3 percent a year to, say, 4 percent, only 160,000 manufacturing jobs would be in jeopardy in a year, and we ought surely to be able to find ways of replacing these jobs by new ones in new industries or in nonmanufacturing occupations. At least I suggest this is a manageable social problem.

I do not suggest that it is easy. But, surely, it is worth substantial efforts, in view of the great benefits which would result from increased industrial production, to explore ways of relocating and retraining workers, of creating—temporarily at least—new jobs through an enlarged public works program, or in other ways, and developing methods of temporary relief to reduce suffering and hardship.

Finding new markets

Yet we face a curious paradox. The primary requirement in reducing unemployment is to increase total production so that at present or even increased productivity levels (output per man-hour) all workers would be employed.

But to increase manufacturing output—even up to present capacity—requires new markets. Our steel and automobile industries could now produce a much larger volume of goods. But they are now producing all they can sell. The same is true in many other industries. The problem is now not how to produce more, but where to sell more.

Only two markets are available—foreign and domestic. Both require expansion. Many foreign countries need more of our products—but, for one reason or another, they cannot buy them. There are many domestic needs unfilled too. We need more schools, hospitals, highways, housing, and many other things. Surely it is an economic problem worthy of our best efforts to solve to bring the demand for needed products (and the resources to pay for them) up to the level of our production capacity—up, indeed, to levels where our productivity will have to be further increased and still retain full employment. The problem of satisfying the needs of the people—and the needs of other people in the world—is no longer a technical one, but an economic (or political) one. Possibly this is the first time in world history that this has been true. Possibly conventional methods of expanding markets—methods based on past experience—are no longer applicable or adequate. New ways must be found to place more purchasing power in the hands of those individuals, those communities, and those nations which still have desperate needs. Then, and only then, will our technical achievements be put to full use.

Worker shortage and surplus

There is one more paradox in the present situation in the United States. We find substantial unemployment among workers—but substantial shortages of scientists, engineers, teachers, technicians, and others in service occupations. Unfortunately, an unskilled laborer cannot usually be converted into a teacher or engineer. Some, however, can be trained to higher or different levels of skills. Yet the challenge we face in the future is to encourage our young people in such a way that a much larger number can train themselves to fill positions in which there are permanent and growing shortages, so that the imbalance we now face will in the long run be alleviated.

EDUCATIONAL PROBLEMS

This brings me to education. How can we create an educational system which will prepare our young people—and older ones too—to understand the new challenges and new opportunities that advancing knowledge brings so we may capitalize on its benefits, reduce its evil and painful side effects, and give all citizens the possibility of engaging in rewarding occupations and living fruitful lives?

It is a tremendous problem—but we start with a tremendous asset. We now have a system which provides free education to every child (except the severely handicapped) through at least his fifteenth year of age. In most cases it may go to the seventeenth year—and, for most of those qualified, through college, and even to the Ph.D. Granted that there are weaknesses, inequities, and dark spots, still the system is in being. Our job is not to create it, but to improve it and adapt it better to our needs.

Unfortunately, even this is a colossal task. For our system—fine as it is, compared to any other in history or in the world today—is woefully short of where it should be to meet the problems of this century and the next. Let me list a few problems.

In an era heavily dependent for future advance in human welfare on scientific and engineering research, we need great numbers of highly talented and thoroughly educated young men and women. We are not getting enough of them. Talents fail to be discovered at an early age; opportunities are denied to many for many reasons (witness, for example, the small number of Negroes in graduate schools—and the small number

of women). Fortunately, great advances in university and graduate education are in process. But progress in identification and encouragement of
high talent still lags.

During the past years there has been an enormous increase in the demand for a college education on the part of the young people of America.
It was only sixty years ago that only between five and ten percent of
the young people of college age actually attended college. Today the
figure is running toward thirty-five percent, and has actually reached
fifty percent in certain areas.

There are many reasons for this. Sixty years ago a college education
was sought primarily by the sons and daughters of preachers, teachers
and lawyers—in general, by those who could afford its cost and those
whose cultural and home backgrounds produced the necessary motivations and desires. A large number of those who went to college intended
also to follow careers in these professions. Gradually, however, as the
need for unskilled workers in industry declined, as the service industries
built up, the need for educated "white-collar workers" expanded, and
with it the college population expanded also. During the depression of
the 1930's there was, of course, a real overproduction of college graduates,
and many of them could not find jobs. There was a strongly expressed
fear that we were going to have an overproduction of the educated
classes. But, at that time, jobs were scarce for the noneducated worker
also.

A miraculous change has occurred since 1940. College graduates are
now in short supply, and the nation's greatly increased prosperity has
brought the desire for more education to vast numbers of young people,
even though not all are primarily interested in its enhancement of their
career opportunities. Education is now regarded as a "good thing" for
every man and woman, for it helps in living a more interesting life. This
should be encouraged, for encouraging more able young people to go
to college will reduce shortages of such workers and, at the same time,
reduce the surplus of the unskilled.

But, far beyond that, a technologically advanced nation requires an
educated body of citizens. When every man on the street is concerned
about nuclear war or fallout, about automation, or space; when every
family has possession of dozens of the products of modern technology,
ranging from an automobile to a television set, automatic toaster, and
electric clock; when every citizen must vote for candidates for public
office, who in turn must make decisions on matters of national defense,
atomic power, space exploration, the regulation of industry, communication, and transport, it is clear that an educated citizenry is an essential
national requirement.

Yet our educational system has lagged in providing its students with
adequate understanding of modern science and technology. How many

people—even college graduates—understand what is meant by fallout, by radiation, by space exploration? How many are sufficiently well-informed on the problems of human health and hygiene that they do not become victims of the quack doctor, the fraudulent seller of drugs or food fads? Think how many people spend their hard-earned cash on products either harmful or useless in solving health problems. How many people understand the nature of science and technology, and what the advances in knowledge in these fields have meant to the human race in recent generations? Our educational system has far to go to catch up with the needs of modern civilization.

It is, however, in our primary and secondary schools that our more serious problems lie. I have mentioned that it is here that high talent in every field needs to be discovered, encouraged, and challenged. But here, too, must all types and all levels of abilities and interests be recognized and guided. A research engineer may be needed to develop a new automation device for industry; but a dozen competent electronic technicians must be available to keep it working. Throughout the whole economy, in fact, competent technicians are required to keep our factories going, our automobiles running, our washing machines washing, our power stations, railroads, airplanes, telephones, and a hundred other essential devices or services properly operating. Are we finding and training such people—and encouraging them to apply their talents in these directions? Or do we expect all our young people to be research scientists or doctors or bankers or salesmen? Dr. James Conant has called attention to the problem of the social pressures in suburban high schools to "get into college"—at all costs. Thus, many a potentially good automobile mechanic becomes an unhappy or second-rate salesman. Where are the vast numbers of fine technical institutes that our industrial society so urgently needs? Without them, boys with fine mechanical or manual aptitudes, not suited for or interested in purely academic training, drift into the ranks of unskilled labor—fine candidates for unemployment when technical advances eliminate their jobs. This is a tragic waste—and a substantial impediment to an advancing industry which needs versatile mechanical skills and is finding less need for the unskilled or the unversatile. Here is an essential key to reducing the pains of dislocation brought on by automation—and we have scarcely made a start in bringing this essential aspect of our educational system into being.

Training the industrial work force

What is it, after all, that mechanization or automation in industry does as far as the worker is concerned? Principally, it relieves the worker of the routine and the repetitive physical and mental tasks. The worker who does nothing but pull a lever, tighten a bolt, or solder a joint may no longer be needed—or may not be needed in such great numbers—when automatic equipment assists in, or takes over, such operations. But, by the same token, more workers will be required to manufacture the automatic equipment, to operate, maintain, and repair it, and be ready to perform both manual and mental operations which require experience, skill, wisdom, and judgment. In the long run, the number of workers required by a mechanized industry will be greater than the number in unmechanized industry, as has been frequently proved to be the case. However, the level of skills required has been gradually increasing, and will continue to increase. More skilled artisans, more technicians and mechanics, more skilled operators of complex machines and equipment will be needed. Most of all, workers will be required with versatile skills, who can swing from one type of skilled task to another as the nature of manufacturing processes changes, or as new types of industries arise and old ones decline. There is a vast problem of training and retraining present adult workers, and, even more important, a future problem in helping young students become skilled and versatile workers.

The ranks of the unemployed are being swollen every year by young men and women who leave school at too early a stage—to a large extent because their school experience has not matched their interests or challenged their abilities. Here is a critical point at which our society can well afford to focus great efforts to prevent this waste of human resources.

A major educational problem associated with the advance of technology in industry is the education and training of the unskilled and the semi-skilled workers. Substantial relief in the problem of technological employment could be attained if industry would establish classes and educational programs for retraining of those whose skills have been displaced through mechanization. There are many operations connected with a mechanized factory or shop in which a few weeks or a few months of training would enable the worker to shift from a displaced task to a new one. A characteristic of many aspects of mechanization is that machines may be operated by those of only a moderate amount of training, provided there are highly skilled workers to do the more complex maintenance operations.

Moreover, continued training programs can enable workers to advance from less skilled to more highly skilled operations, and also to acquire an increased versatility of skill so their displacement by new mechanization is less likely. Every type of industry offers special problems and opportunities in this field, but the cooperative effort of management and labor should be directed at a study of the problem, and the introduction of training programs would result in a more effective and a more versatile working force. The spectacular success of many industrial training programs during the war should provide all the proof that is needed that men and women can be trained for a variety of skills in a relatively short period, provided the program is properly managed.

Suggested improvements

Many things can be done to match our educational system to our needs. Here are a few:

1. Improve our public schools all along the line, eliminating blighted conditions in slums and rural areas, providing equal opportunities for all children of the nation.

2. Improve the general education in the elementary schools, including mathematics, science, and foreign language along with basic subjects.

3. Improve attention to individual aptitudes and talents, guiding the academically gifted to college preparation, the manually or technically gifted to technical high schools, junior colleges, or institutes.

4. Greatly expand the technical institutes or technical training in high school or junior college to provide broad education for technicians, mechanics, and other highly skilled trades, with emphasis on versatility of skills.

5. Expand training courses in industry to develop suitable skills for the modern industrial worker, and retraining opportunities for displaced workers.

6. Expand and improve the colleges and universities to accommodate the growing college population and to prepare students more adequately for life in the modern world.

7. Eliminate racial and other discrimination in all the educational system.

8. Expand the graduate and professional schools to meet the needs for scientists, engineers, doctors, psychologists, social scientists, teachers, and other professional personnel.

All of these changes should be aimed at aiding young people (and adults too) to (1) understand the modern world, and thus be better and more intelligent citizens, (2) prepare them for work and career opportunities which now exist, (3) enhance their abilities to make more fruitful use of their leisure time.

That these changes will cost money and will require large numbers of adequately trained teachers goes without saying. It may be that new methods of financing education will have to be evolved. But the economic and social benefits to be attained are enormous—well worth the added costs. It is not too much to say that an adequate educational system is essential to an industrial society—both to advance its technology and to cope with resulting social and human problems. Man is still the master of the machine. A better educated man can be a better master.

Conclusion

To repeat: scientific and technological knowledge and its applications have brought new security, new comforts, new dignity within the reach of human beings. They have brought in sight the day of elimination of most kinds of unskilled hand labor—and have thus elevated the status and the dignity of the working man—if he is suitably educated to perform more skilled and more interesting tasks. They have also increased the need for and social importance of the highly talented and the well educated—the teachers, the scientists, engineers, doctors, lawyers, industrial managers. Our educational system and our social and political institutions and practices face a great challenge in helping us—and all the world—meet these new opportunities.

Floyd C. Mann

3

Psychological and Organizational Impacts

We will look at the impact on the organization and individuals of recent developments in technology in plant and office. We will identify what changes have occurred in the environment of the worker and note how these appear to be affecting his life. In a field rampant with speculation and unverified hypotheses, we will try to describe the effects of the new breakthroughs in technology by drawing primarily from empirical research findings.

Our primary concern will be with the psychological and social consequences of technological change. We will bear in mind that what is good for the individual may be just the opposite for the total society of which he is a part. Most important of all, we will have to remember that our evidence is anything but conclusive. Our facts have both temporal and

FLOYD C. MANN *is an industrial social psychologist at The University of Michigan. As a program director at the Institute for Social Research, he is responsible for studies of organizational change and effectiveness, and industrial mental health. He is also a member of the Department of Psychology. His early training was in sociology and economics. During World War II, Professor Mann was with the Bureau of Labor Statistics in Washington, D.C.*

This chapter draws on the findings of other social scientists. The synopses presented here have attempted to reproduce the spirit, stance, and approach of each researcher, and the author has made use of their individual vocabularies and phrases. Major references and quotations are indicated as such, but the indebtedness goes beyond this. Drs. Robert L. Kahn and Franklin W. Neff carefully reviewed a draft of this chapter and Mrs. Margery Sanford added materially to its readability.

spatial qualifications. They have been extracted from the fast-moving technological surge in the United States in the last fifteen years.

In spite of the thousands of articles that have been written in the last fifteen years about automation, there are relatively few careful empirical studies of the changes occurring in plant, factory and office. We propose to present here many of the principal findings from three investigations of automation in the plant and three investigations in the office.

AUTOMATION IN FACTORY AND PLANT

We are investing comparatively little to extend and deepen our knowledge of the increasingly industrial times through which we are passing. The number of social research units devoting efforts to unraveling the multiple effects of the new technological changes on individuals, organizations and society can probably be numbered on one hand.

As might be expected, different researchers have used different methods and concentrated on different aspects of these industrial technological developments. Some have been more concerned with how the changes were handled than with the effects; some have looked through the eyes of management, others through the employees. The findings of the investigators in this section are based on their intensive case studies of a single plant; there have been few studies of a number of organizational sites in search of broader generalizations. Much of the work has been done using exploratory or, at best, semi-structured interviews, although this has occasionally been supplemented with some attempts at systematic measurement. These differences are worth noting; they affect markedly the range and quality of material from which we work. In each study we will try to abstract what appear to be the more permanent effects of automation on the individual and the organization—for it is in these that we are primarily interested.

A semi-automatic steel tube mill [1]

This is an account of the start-up of the first continuous seamless pipe mill in the United States—a study of a type of "transfer automation." A piece of steel was conveyed automatically through five machining processes and formed into a steel pipe of varying specified length and thickness. The mill produced pipe of better quality four times as fast as the conventional mill with fewer than half the men. Nine men for each shift worked as a team to initiate and monitor and—if anything went wrong—to intervene and control the process. The semi-automatic character of the mill, with workers at different stations able to adjust the speed of the operation, resulted in a highly integrated man-machine

[1] Study by Charles R. Walker. See *Toward the Automatic Factory: A Case Study of Men and Machines.* New Haven, Conn.: Yale University Press, 1957.

system in which there had to be a high order of coordination between man and man, and man and machines. Most of the operations could control themselves automatically or be controlled manually. The men were trained informally for their jobs as they worked with the engineers and supervisors in getting the new equipment operating.

In the new mill half as many men were scattered over an area twice as large as in the older ones. They felt more isolated, had less chance to talk face-to-face. There was one less level of supervision between the superintendent and the men, and at the outset this contributed to a closer relationship between men and management. Working conditions were better: greater cleanliness, light, space and air, and less heat and hazard—but with a continuing problem of smoke. The average classification of the jobs was "somewhat lower." After the mill was rolling, the take-home pay of the crews was greater than in the old mills. A group incentive system was employed. With smaller crews, fewer jobs, and lower job classifications, promotional opportunities had decreased and the men felt they had less opportunity to advance. Without technical education, promotion to management seemed less likely.

The men saw the jobs in the new mill as radically different. Jobs were "physically easier," but "mentally harder," demanding alertness, continuous "watching," and thought. Responsibility was seen as much greater, and, initially, there was anxiety over the serious consequences of a wrong move. The men were "jumpy" and uncertain of their own ability to handle the problems of the new mill. After two years most of them felt they had mastered the new automatic system. They had become "used to the jobs," had greatly increased their knowledge of them, and had ceased "being scared." After the plant had been "debugged" and the union-management problems had been worked through, the new mill continued to require somewhat more of a worker's energy than the older equipment. The men were proud of their new competence and liked the "automatics" much better. In fact, they became so adept in handling the mill with new work rhythms that they found "a way to run it faster— and hence earn a larger bonus—on manual than on automatic." But they did this only occasionally.

The change to the new mill meant a change in both functional and social relations with fellow workers. Fewer groups of men worked together on the same unit, and initially the workers did not feel comfortable communicating through a public address system. Together with the demands of the job, this meant less opportunity to talk and visit. A majority felt this made no difference; some disliked it. However, there was as much or more functional interdependence in the new mill. This required interaction and eventually led to the development of highly cooperative, cohesive work teams with strong group feelings.

When the mill was being readied for production, the men rated their relations with supervisors as "better" than in the old mills. They were working together closely to solve problems. This relationship deteriorated and turned to hostility during an extended fight over crew size and incentive rates. After these problems had been settled, hostility disappeared. However, the crews continued to feel that management was unwilling to ask them to help with the solution of production problems, and they resented it.

When the men in this mill were asked whether new plants and mills are a good thing for the working man, two-thirds of them emphasized the negative and saw such improvements as "a real threat to the working man." This was true even after they were getting both the security and high wages of their own new jobs, and they had seen that no one was laid off as a result of the new mills. In spite of the fact that displaced men were retrained and given other jobs at equal pay, in the minds of the men technological improvement was equated with technological unemployment for someone.

An automated automobile engine plant[2]

This was a study of transfer or "Detroit automation"—the type of advanced mechanization where materials are moved by automatic transfer machines from station to station along a line, positioned, machined automatically, and finally assembled. In this case the plant was designed to take castings of engine blocks, cylinder heads, crank shafts, and other parts, and machine and assemble them into an engine. The new plant was highly efficient, producing higher quality engines than the other plants in the same company, with fewer employees, lower scrap rates, lower maintenance costs, and less materials storage and handling charges. There was, however, greater need for preventive maintenance to avoid costly breakdowns of the highly integrated system of transfer machines. The plant was producing 150 engines per hour at the time of the study.

There were 1600 workers in the manufacturing operations; 1100 were working in automated departments. Most of them had transferred from older plants through exercising seniority rights. The characteristics of the work forces in the new and the older plants were similar. Rates of turnover, absences, and grievances were comparable.

The proportion of jobs in the skilled trades was higher in the new plant. No training program was established for machine operators since management "did not feel that new skills were required in semi-skilled classifications on automated lines." Some specialized training was given to job setters and machine repairmen. "Automation did not have any appreciable effect on the wage structure of this plant." In automated

---

[2] Study by William A. Faunce. See *Automation in the Automobile Industry: Some Consequences for In-Plant Union-Management Relationships.* Unpublished doctoral dissertation, Wayne State University, 1957, and *The Automobile Industry: A Case Study in Automation.* In H. B. Jacobson and J. S. Roucek (eds.), *Automation and Society.* New York: Philosophical Library, 1959.

departments, however, "a larger proportion of the workers received job classifications with higher hourly wage rates." Higher rates for some machine operation jobs were negotiated, but "no major wage changes were made." One new job classification was established—"console operator." This was for the workers who were to watch "a panel of lights signaling operations along a complete transfer line."

The job content and work environment in the new plant were different. Workers, comparing their previous job in nonautomated plants with their present jobs, reported (1) much closer and more constant attention required by the new jobs, (2) even fewer jobs where work was paced by the operator, (3) greater distance between work stations in the new plant, and (4) fewer jobs involving teamwork. These changes affected patterns of social relations on the job. Many workers were "virtually isolated socially." There was less personal contact within smaller groups and less identification with a particular work group. On the other hand, workers reported closer supervision from all levels. The change in supervision appeared to have been "a result of both a decrease in the number of workers per foreman and an increase in the amount of time spent by each foreman in direct supervision of the line."

This reduction of social interaction and an increase in supervision were two sources of worker dissatisfaction. Workers also reported greater tension because of higher demands on their attention and a faster production rate. They did not like the reduction in their control of the work pace or the feeling of separation from the work process. Nevertheless, a majority of them preferred their present automated jobs. They liked the decrease in amount of materials-handling, and reported that their jobs had greater interest. There was little difference between the working conditions in the new and older plants except some evidence of a higher noise level. Although they believed that automation was putting people out of work, the workers did not feel their own jobs less secure.

The role of the foreman in the automated plant also appeared to change. The workers reported the relationship between them and their foreman had been better on the old job. In the new plant the foreman had to meet increased production schedules without being able to utilize effectively either his acquired human relations skills or the knowledge he had accumulated about conventional machining processes. This was thought to have contributed to the tensions in the relationship with the workers.

Automated power plants[3]

This was a comparative study of two power plants—one with increased mechanization, integration of function, and more frequent use of auto-

[3] Study by F. C. Mann and L. R. Hoffman. See *Automation and the Worker: A Study of Social Change in Power Plants.* New York: Holt, Rinehart & Winston, Inc., 1960.

matic equipment and feedback control devices—to identify some of the probable effects of automation on workers and organizations. The new plant had the most modern boiler-turbine-generator units in the United States; it could generate a third more electricity with a working force of only slightly more than half the number manning the older plant. The actual complement of operators per shift in the new plant was 15, as compared to 49 in the older plant. The integration of boiler and turbine operations and automatic controls had permitted the centralization of many operations at a few major control rooms in the new plant. Instead of working at widely scattered and isolated stations throughout the plant, many men worked with others in front of panels of dials and switches. Working conditions in the new plant were markedly better than in the old plant, especially in terms of cleanliness, ventilation, and temperature. Top hourly rates for operators in the new plant were from 19 to 46 cents higher than in the older plant.

Indirect measures of pride and prestige indicated that men in the new plant were proud of their plant and its importance in the total system. Workers in the new plant were more satisfied with their promotional progress and their wages. Both men and foremen felt they had more to say about how things were done than those in the older plant. More men than in the old plant evaluated favorably the administrative and human relations skills of the front-office managers. The men in the new plant also differed in background characteristics and social values. In general, they were younger, more educated, had fewer years of service, and were more interested in being part of a rapidly expanding company where new jobs were being created and the pace was being set for other companies. These were some of the factors which contributed to a higher level of job satisfaction in the new than in the old plant. Others were changes in the structure of jobs, a new shift work pattern, and the character of supervision in the new plant. The absence rates of the men in the new plant were significantly lower than their past absence rates in the older plant.

The operating jobs were organized in an entirely different manner in the new plant. Part of this was the direct result of the technological design of this plant, part stemmed from a management decision to try for greater organizational flexibility in manning it. In the older plant, three major operating groups handled the three production functions of boiler, turbine and condensor, and electrical operations. The integration of boiler and turbine functions and their controls in the new plant meant that operators would have to handle both turbines and boilers. This led the company to examine the possibility of further enlarging the operating jobs to include the electrical operating as well. Rotation among different control rooms and stations was originally instituted as a part of the training program for the new jobs. This practice was continued with the men changing positions weekly. Job content was thus changed by both job enlargement and job rotation. When those operators who had worked under the job structure of the old plants were compared with the operators still in the older plant, it was found that the men in the new plant felt they had much more responsibility now, their jobs required more training, they spent more time doing things they were skilled at, and more time learning new things. More of these operators also felt they had opportunities for greater physical mobility around the plant and more contact with other men now. All said their job was more interesting and satisfying now than several years ago.

Accompanying these changes in job content was a greater degree of interdependence among the operators in the new plant and between the men and their foreman. More men in the new plant than in the older one reported they depended on other men in their work group and on their foreman for suggestions and advice. More also saw their foreman depending on them for suggestions and advice on handling job problems.

Significantly more operators in the more automated plant admitted their work made them nervous and that they were "on edge" when an important piece of equipment was being started up or shut down. Feelings of interdependence were found to be directly related to feelings of nervousness and tension on the job. Dependence on other operators was also related to satisfaction with training. Those who reported having to depend on others "a great deal" or "quite a lot" were also dissatisfied with the training they had received for their new jobs. An examination of workers' attitudes toward the training program suggested that this tension could have been lessened if more attention had been devoted to ensuring on-the-job practical experience in addition to the formal classroom training.

About half of the men in these two power plants worked on rotating work schedules around the clock—such continuous operations are a common characteristic of highly automated systems. The shift schedules in each plant were markedly different. Both were eight-hour work days, but in the new plant the men worked for seven consecutive days, had a few days off, and then returned to another shift, while in the old plant shifts rotated only after a month. Few men in either plant liked shift work; they either "did not mind it" or disliked it. In spite of the generally negative attitude toward shift work, almost two and a half times as many men in the new plant with its seven-day rotation pattern said they liked or did not mind shift work. In both plants the shift workers complained of the way these rotation patterns disrupted the basic body rhythms of sleeping and eating, and it was clear that they got together with their friends less often than nonshift workers. The men in the new plant, however, reported that they adjusted to shift changes more rapidly than did the workers in the old plant, that their families less often disliked their working shifts and felt less strongly about it, and they visited with their friends more frequently than did the workers in the old plant. The more tolerant attitudes of these men toward shift work appeared to be attributable to the less disruptive effects of weekly rotation on their family and social life.

No evidence was found at the time of this study that the more complex equipment in the automated plant resulted in a higher evaluation of the technical competence of the supervisors there than in the older plant. The employees in both plants felt that the most satisfactory supervisors were those who were considerate of them, who assisted them in getting ahead in the company, and who asked for their ideas in handling work problems. In the new plant the human relations skills of the supervisors were even more related to their employees' satisfactions with them than in the old.

The technological changes incorporated in the new plant brought about a number of changes in the company's organizational structure. The structure within the older plant was modified; the relationship among the plants, and between the production department and several other closely related departments, was reshaped. Thus the introduction of a new plant into one part of the system had important repercussions on other parts of the system. The high costs which would arise from losing the productive capacity of any of the units in the new plant caused the management of the company to expand its program of preventive maintenance by centralizing maintenance operations. The impact of this reorganization was felt most strongly by the men in top maintenance positions in the power plants and by the maintenance men who remained in the service groups at each plant. The construction of the automated power plant was also seen as a threat to worker job security in the older plants of the system. Decreasing operating loads and a sense of increasing obsolescence of skills caused the operators in the older plant to be concerned about the security of their future in the company.

Within the new power plant the reduction in the number of levels of supervision appeared to have effects on the relative influence of different groups and on the degree of communication in that plant. There was greater satisfaction with the amount of communication from the top of the plant organization to the nonsupervisory employees, and a greater sharing of the decision-making power by the top staff of the plant with the foremen and the workers. Structural changes in the plant design also seem to have had effects on the feelings of the workers about the other workers of their groups. The centralization of operating controls appears to have had positive effects in the creation of greater group unity among the operators.

The impact in factory and plant

The synopses of these studies focus our attention on the following points.

1. Basic changes in technology mean major changes in the division of labor and the content of jobs. In the less automated systems, such as the engine plant and the semi-automated tube mill, this means workers have to pay closer and more constant attention to the new jobs. There is less physical effort, less handling of heavy materials, but more mental effort. In these situations, employees and machines are highly interdependent man-machine systems. This unrelenting demand for alert watching and thought contributes to the heightened feelings of tension and uneasiness —especially at the outset. In the most highly automated systems where machines do their own monitoring and adjusting of controls, such as in the new power plant, workers also find they have to be alert and ready for action because of the speed of operation. Production rates have frequently been removed from the control of the worker and are dependent only upon the physical limitations of the equipment.

The new jobs are generally safer, the worker being more physically separated from the work process. High production rates, however, may reintroduce some hazards in the continuous process plants where a small failure in the system may compound to frightening proportions in a matter of seconds.

Greater system integration, with fewer workers manning it, typically means a single member has responsibility for a larger span of the line. While an operator's work may involve only patroling and inspecting a system when all is functioning properly, he is expected to recognize an incipient crisis and to do "the right thing." Responsibility of this character requires more of a systemic sense—knowledge and competence of a depth essential to handle a highly interlocked system of machines, and perhaps of machines and men.

The integration of what were formerly more discrete units of equipment also means the integration of jobs. Old boundaries between tasks are being wiped out as jobs are combined and enlarged. Workers are asked to perform a wider range of duties, some of higher caliber.

It is highly significant that many of the workers in these new plants are finding their jobs not only more demanding, but providing greater variety and interest, more challenge, and increased opportunity to learn. With the goals of greater system integration and efficiency, the design engineer may have accomplished what the industrial engineer failed to do—provide the worker with an environment of tasks appropriate to the skills of a human.

Whether these effects of the change in the content of jobs are temporary or permanent cannot be answered from research findings yet. The start-up of a new equipment complex is without doubt an exciting period of growth and new experiences. Supervisors and men are learning their new roles. It is likely that the new jobs will continue to demand a high level of attention and alertness of the worker long after the start-up and shake-down phases are past. It is not yet clear, however, whether these new jobs will continue to provide more variety, challenge, and opportunity to develop when the equipment is running smoothly.

   2. Change in the structure of jobs affects the social relations among workers. In the less automated systems, there is greater physical distance among work stations and less contact between workers. The number working together in a cluster is far fewer than on preautomated production lines. Many workers in plants like the engine and tube mill are so isolated that they cannot directly talk with one another; friendships are more difficult to establish.

   In the more continuous process plants, the men may work together in twos or threes before massive control panels, or work "on patrol" out of such rooms. Here too the pace of the production process and the responsibility of the job afford little opportunity to talk about anything other than immediate job matters. With a smaller number of men operating these plants and greater opportunities for movement about them, the men may know the names of a higher proportion of their co-workers but know very little about them as individuals.

   The most advanced production processes are no longer so dependent upon the establishment of work teams with a strong sense of cohesiveness. Since workers vary markedly in their needs for affiliation, this change is a source of dissatisfaction for some men but not for others.

   3. Working conditions are typically better. New plants and larger equipment complexes generally mean improved physical conditions— clean new machines, fresh paint, better lights, and more space and air. The highly sensitive monitoring instruments often require that the rooms containing control consoles and sometimes whole buildings be kept at even temperature; air conditioning is not uncommon. Less likelihood of minor bodily injury has already been mentioned. In general, the more mechanization and automation, the better the physical working conditions.

   4. Technologically advanced plants demand different supervisory skills. Usually both workers and management recognize that new plants demand a high order of technical competence from supervisors. There is no substitute for knowing how the system is designed and how it functions. In a crisis, the supervisor must be able to give appropriate orders. Human relations skills are not unimportant but technical know-how may be absolutely essential.

   With system integration, there are fewer levels of supervision and fewer workers. This, together with markedly greater responsibility for costly equipment and the imperative of avoiding unscheduled shutdowns, causes an increase in time spent by each foreman in direct supervision. Also there is often closer supervision by all levels.

   The men in highly automated plants may feel a better communication between them and top plant management because of few levels, but simultaneously feel supervised more closely. The integration of the operation also places a premium on managerial and supervisory planning. Schedules are generally tighter and more demanding.

Supervisors in new plants may feel particularly pressed as they find that their human relations skills are not so important, since neither the individual nor the group affects so directly the production process, and their technical skills, accumulated in more conventional plants, are outmoded. The continuing importance of the human relations skills of the supervisor is pointed up by the recognition by men and supervisors alike that changes in job content have resulted in a greater interdependence, and that each must necessarily (and especially in the beginning stages of a new plant) get the ideas of the other.

The supervisor must be sure that his men are getting the training necessary to be at ease. The change from preautomated to the least automated jobs may not require much additional training, as we have seen in the case of the engine plant. However, there is ample evidence that a totally new environment of massive machinery capable of considerably higher speeds of operation than the operator has ever encountered before can elicit a good deal of apprehension. Feeling greater interdependence, but not knowing for sure what the other men or supervisors know or do not know, creates uneasiness and anxiety. The supervisor concerned with both the proper functioning of the plant and the health of the members of his work force as individuals needs to be certain that his own training and that of his men is adequate.

5. Changes in the structure of jobs mean changes in career patterns, channels of promotion, and job security. With smaller work forces, fewer job classes, fewer levels of supervision, and increasingly complex technical work environments, many workers feel the promotional ladders they had planned to climb are shortened or shattered. There is less opportunity for advancement into supervisory positions; career lines are often destroyed. Accumulated skills may be wiped out, and requirements substituted which the worker does not have the education to acquire.

Workers in the new plants are usually satisfied with their promotions to date, but not so sure of their future. Workers left in the older plants are less satisfied with present progress and much less sanguine about the future.

The outlook of the men in the new plants regarding job security is also extremely different from the outlook of those in the older plants. They recognize that in a rapidly changing technological sea, they have made it into a relatively safe port. Since the new equipment is economically more efficient, the capital costs are fixed, and the labor costs of operation relatively insignificant, they know that they will be the last to be affected by an economic recession. They recognize that technological change may mean technological unemployment for other workers. They may be concerned about this as a general problem in other plants or the society at large, but they see a secure, continuous future of employment for themselves in their advanced plant. They "have it made."

In the older plants it is just the opposite. Depending upon the age of their plant, the men sense more or less keenly that the starting up of a new unit—particularly within a relatively closed system—has moved their plant a giant step toward the day when it will be obsolete. To these men, this obsolescence means obsolescence of their own skills. They know their jobs are becoming less secure. A waning plant may mean the slow erosion of status, and occupational identity and meaningfulness in our industrial society.

6. *Work in more advanced technological plants is generally rewarded with higher pay.* While there is typically little up-grading of jobs under automation, workers are generally paid a little more per hour than in less automated plants. With self-regulating mechanisms controlling machine complexes and built-in rates of production, there is little the worker can do in the most advanced systems to augment quantity or quality of a product. Individual or small group incentive systems are no longer useful. Each worker's role in the total system is of greater significance, however, and the presence of each man at each scheduled work period is relatively more important in these plants. With smaller work forces, the problem of getting a man at the last moment to fill in a shift turn is greater administratively than in older plants.

There are, of course, a number of other factors contributing to slightly higher rates of pay. Where the workers are organized, the union leadership pushes for higher wages for jobs in the new plants. Where workers have not been organized, management for any of a number of reasons (to compensate the men for working at new tasks in new job environments, to overcome resistance to change, to forestall the organization of personnel, or to share the economic gains of the new system) pays higher wage rates.

7. *Work in new plants generally carries more prestige.* To be working in one of the most technologically advanced plants in the world is psychologically rewarding. Such a plant is usually the show-place of the company. Visiting dignitaries are escorted through; classes of school children look wide-eyed at evidence of our industrial prowess and at the men who direct such massive complexes. Families of the workers volunteer with pride that one of their members works at *the* new plant. In this society where science and innovation are highly valued, the worker himself takes pride in being a part of the "new team." While these same men may have some question about their ability to meet the new requirements, they are nonetheless proud to be associated with such a plant.

8. *Work in the most technologically advanced plants is likely to require around-the-clock operations.* With larger capital investments relative to labor costs, the scheduling of work for 24-hour operation becomes more

prevalent. It is too soon to say how much of the labor force will be on work schedules discordant with the basic patterns of working in the day, recreating in the evening, and sleeping at night. Whether the proportion will be higher or lower, it is clear that some workers and their families will be asked to make the sizable physiological and social adjustments required to man these plants 24 hours a day.

Working when nearly all the rest of the community is not working is generally not very satisfactory to man, wife, or family. Few men in continuous process plants like shift work; their wives and families feel much the same. Especially with rotating shifts, basic body rhythms are disturbed. Work schedules "at odds" with the community affect markedly, and usually negatively, the worker's performance of his role as husband, father, friend, and responsible citizen. It seems increasingly clear that the demands of shift work sharpen mind-body conflicts: physical man tries to cope with the loss of sleep, appetite, and regularity of body function, while social man must meet obligations to his family and the social order.

AUTOMATION IN THE OFFICE

Technological changes are bringing important and spectacular transformations to plant and factory. But automation may have its biggest initial human impact in the office. We were not prepared for the scientific breakthroughs in the late 1940's which greatly modified the conceptualization, quantification, and processing of information. This revolution has initiated a number of trends which are culminating today in major technological changes in the office. Electronic data processing (EDP) equipment is now organizing and computing information at prodigious rates. The white collar worker, who heretofore has had to respond only occasionally and marginally to the intrusions of technology, is now confronted with the demand to relate to a machine environment. In some respects he is clearly less well prepared for this than was the blue collar worker, his counterpart in the factory.

First Quantitative Case Study[4]

This is a study of the effects of a small or "medium" computer (IBM 650) in the statistical department of a medium-size casualty insurance company. The change-over was completed in half a year. Only two departments were materially affected: the statistical department which

---

[4] Study by Einar Hardin. See "Computer Automation, Work Environment, and Employee Satisfaction: A Case Study." *Industrial & Labor Relations Review*, 1960, 13 (4), 557-567.

assumed responsibility for the new equipment, and the automobile underwriting department, much of whose work was taken over by the machine. Organizationally the principal changes were the creation of a separate policy-processing division within the statistical department, the setting and enforcement of deadlines for completion of work, the rotation of personnel within the division to promote flexibility of personnel assignment. Affected and unaffected departments were compared with respect to employee feelings about job changes. Findings were based on data collected after the conversion was essentially completed.

More employees in the affected departments reported that the computer had had an impact on their job as a whole and on specific aspects of the job than the employees in the unaffected departments. The two groups differed very little in the direction of the changes they saw in their job. More in the affected departments felt the amount of variety in their work had increased; fewer in the same group felt the amount of pay they received had increased.

Employees in the affected and unaffected departments did not differ in feelings about the impact of the computer or net changes in specific aspects of their jobs. Affected departments tended to show more dissatisfaction with their jobs after the installation, but the differences were small. These findings were interpreted as providing little support for the hypothesis that changes in job content caused by computer automation differ sharply in frequency or direction from those which occur normally with everyday organizational changes.

Second Quantitative Case Study[5]

This is another questionnaire study of the impact of an IBM 650 on a medium-size insurance company in a small midwestern city. Again the change-over was essentially completed within six months. Employees were given assurances that the new equipment would not jeopardize any person's job. Those whose tasks were to be affected directly were given training in the new work procedures. Three different groups of departments were identified: those where the impact would be the greatest—the computer area; those whose personnel either lost many tasks to the computer or had to learn new forms, codes, and procedures; and unaffected departments where the change had no effect. During the period of the change-over, other changes were postponed in the unaffected departments, which therefore serve as a reasonably good control group. Before-and-after questionnaires were filled out by 246 employees.

The computer was seen as affecting the work environments of employees in a number of respects, but the over-all change was similar in

    [5] Study by Einar Hardin. See "The Reactions of Employees to Office Automation." *Monthly Labor Review*, 1960, 83, 925-932.

the three departmental groupings. Positive attitudes toward the computer were common; employees generally liked the changes in their job content. Sixty-one percent of the employees in both the computer area and other affected departments felt the change-over had been only slightly disrupting or not at all disrupting, while 20 percent saw it as quite disrupting, and only 9 percent felt it to be very disrupting. Employees in the computer area tended to become less satisfied with the administration of the change, while those in other affected departments tended to become less satisfied with intrinsic job aspects. Most departmental differences in job satisfaction change were slight. That the affected departments and unaffected departments were found to differ little in perceived jobs changes, in feelings about these changes, and in changes in job satisfaction suggests that the installation of an IBM 650 computer does not differ much from other types of office change in its impact on the nature of the job and the work environment.

Change-over to large computer[6]

This is a multi-phase study of the effects of a change-over to two small computers (IBM 650's) and then one large-scale computer (IBM 705) over a period of five years in a group of accounting and sales departments in a large electric power company. Findings concerning the long period of conversion and how it was handled are based on unstructured interviews, but before-and-after measures from questionnaires with all levels of personnel were also employed to determine the effects of this change.

The change-over to electronic equipment affected two principal subsystems—record-keeping and customer contacts. The capacity of the equipment was such that it was possible to rethink and redesign major sectors of the company work. Functions and employees were shifted between the accounting and sales divisions; a major reorganization of activities and responsibilities occurred within the accounting area. Work sections and departmental lines were redrawn, new departments created, and a level of management added.

Equilibrium and relative stability gave way dramatically to high activity and increased tempo during installation, testing, and conversion before the organization settled again into a "steady-state." During the transition period there were the usual problems accompanying a major technological

[6] Study by F. C. Mann and L. K. Williams. See "Organizational Impact of White Collar Automation." *Industrial Relations Research Association Annual Proceedings,* 1958, Publication No. 22, 59-69, and "Observations on the Dynamics of a Change to Electronic Data Processing Equipment." *Administrative Science Quarterly,* 1960, 5, (2) 217-256, and "Some Effects of the Changing Work Environment in the Office." *Journal of Social Issues,* 1962, 18 (3).

change—extensive overtime, training of personnel for new jobs, and the mounting pressures of meeting deadlines that had been established long before there was any depth of understanding of the problems. In many ways it was a period of heroic effort as supervisory and non-supervisory employees worked to establish a totally new system of procedures, to test and begin to operate it, and maintain the old system until the time to change over.

This change-over to electronic data processing increased markedly the level of formalization within the organization. Work was further rationalized. Rules and regulations were substituted for individual decision-making. With greater integration of the system, more control and responsibility for the decisions were centralized. Variations in work pace and process were further restricted. Deadlines became more important, standards of performance higher and more rigidly enforced. Absences and tardiness became increasingly disruptive. EDP eliminated not only some of the more routine menial jobs, but also higher grade jobs where decisions had formerly been made within a relatively restricted range of alternatives. The net effect was essentially no change in the average job grade, except in the electronic data programming area. Those were marked changes in channels of promotion and career within the company. Some shift work was also introduced.

Categories of jobs which existed before the electronic equipment were compared with those that existed afterwards. This analysis demonstrated that the new jobs require a greater amount of risk (in that errors cost more in time and dollars) and a greater understanding of the total system. A greater degree of personal contact among members of any work group and a greater degree of interdependence were also characteristic of the new jobs. There was also an increase in the opportunity to detect specific errors and find out who made them. In the aggregate, the introduction of EDP equipment appeared to mean the general tightening of the task structure of the office.

Significantly more of the employees working at jobs integral to the new 705 system, in contrast to those on jobs not related to the new system, reported greater satisfaction with job responsibility, more variety and change, and greater opportunities to learn new things. Those working in highly integrated jobs also saw their jobs as more important now. Other analyses show these employees to be aware that performance standards were tighter and more rigidly enforced, that there were more deadlines which were more important.

In general, these data lead toward the conclusion that while employees in the new work environment had more interesting and challenging jobs than earlier, the greater exposure to risk and the tighter performance standards negated the attractive aspects of the change in the content of the job.

Other analyses showed that after the change the office workers felt that top management was less interested in them as individual employees. Significantly higher proportions believed their future looked somewhat worse, and they were worried about temporary layoffs or losing their jobs. The nonsupervisory and supervisory men who had been at the very vortex of the extended and intense process of the change-over showed evidence of more psychological and physical anxiety than similar white collar groups in the nation.

Twenty installations of EDP [7]

This study, made in the San Francisco Bay area, is concerned with the impact of electronic data processing equipment on the clerical labor force and the structure of jobs, on individual employees at all levels, on groups of workers, and on the organization as a whole. The findings are based on unstructured interviews over time with top management, supervisory and nonsupervisory personnel, and union officers. The companies ranged from very large to very small; the equipment introduced also varied similarly.

This extensive investigation finds that office automation reduces the number of clerical jobs, does not raise the skill level or grades of jobs, and does not generally provide greater job interest or challenge. The major exception to this is the small group of programmers and systems analysts. While these new occupational groups are higher paid and have interesting jobs, most other supporting jobs are monotonous and increasingly demanding as the paper work flows become more rationalized and integrated with a high-speed computer. The employees hardest hit are the filing clerks, bookkeepers, and their supervisors. Especially vulnerable are the older workers who do not have the required skills or are either unwilling to be retrained for the new jobs or incapable.

In this study EDP is seen as tending to make the office into a "paper-processing factory." Work is more routine, monotonous, pressured, and confining. With a greater demand for accuracy, concern for detail, and sustained high productivity, workers—especially key punch operators—experience a great deal of tension on the job. Contributing to the factory-like atmosphere are the noise and heat of the key punch machines and the auxiliary equipment, the increased measurement of work, the introduction of shift work, and the occasional relocation of workers in new EDP centers in "less desirable areas" outside the central business districts.

The redivision of labor destroys the interaction and interdependence of workers, disrupts group cohesiveness, and hampers the formation of

---

[7] Study by Ida R. Hoos. See "Impact of Automation on Office Workers." *International Labour Review*, 1960, 82, 363-388, and *Automation in the Office*. Washington, D.C.: Public Affairs Press, 1961.

new relationships. The curtailing of branch operations and centralizing of work force employees to give up their jobs or transfer to another city; the relocation of workers in new EDP centers at some distance from the main office buildings breaks ties with those who remain. Two possible outcomes are predicted to be sources of increasing dissatisfaction and the eventual development of *anomie;* a third is the gradual breakdown of the barrier between white collar and blue collar workers, and a change in the former's ideology toward unionization both as a source of job security and social identification.

Automation in these offices also had a marked effect on organizational structure. EDP was seen to be reversing the trend toward decentralization in many firms. The new trend appeared to be toward centralization. Divisional and departmental lines were being affected, operations consolidated, layers of administration reduced. Promotional ladders were reported as materially affected, with some rungs in middle management disappearing. With changes in formal structure and lines of authority, channels of communication were seen as being altered—both formal and informal.

The impact in the office

These summaries provide us with another common point of departure to use in identifying major psychological and social effects of automation in the office.

1. Developments in the theory of information and electronic data processing equipment mean major changes in organizational structure and the division of labor in the office. It appears that the changes brought by the small (or "medium size") computers are qualitatively different from those initiated by the large electronic complexes. A conversion from a standard mechanical punch card system to a small computer (e.g., IBM 650) may bring some shifting of functions within a relatively restricted part of the company, but there is no basic change in the system's division of labor—its departmental lines, the content of jobs, or work flows. Nor do the satisfactions of the people who perform these jobs seem to be significantly affected. Installations take only six months and are felt by employees to be only slightly disruptive. Employees in units losing functions may be slightly less satisfied, those at the center of the change not fully satisfied with the way the change was handled. But there is little evidence of uneasiness about being made superfluous.

The capacity of large electronic complexes to process great masses of information in fractions of seconds with tremendous accuracy, on the other hand, forces the rethinking and redesigning of the organization if full use is to be made of the new technology. Reversals of basic organizational policies toward decentralization are possible. With greater and greater integration, control is centralized, autonomy of branches and intermediate levels of management reduced. This explains why there may be fewer supervisors and fewer administrative levels after a major change-over.

The large computer, the essence of rationality itself, must operate within a highly rationalized system if it is to function effectively. Many of the lower level routine clerical jobs formerly performed by individuals, and even some of the higher level "known criterion" decision-making jobs, are taken over by the equipment. The jobs remaining demand of the white collar worker even more than before in precision and accuracy. The clerks assembling and preparing information for punching must do their work quickly, accurately, and within a narrow range of alternatives —for these tasks, like those of the key punch operators, are integrated with the high speed equipment. Systems analysts and programmers, while their work is not as temporally integrated into a man-machine system as the supporting clerical and punching groups, also have very little latitude in how they perform their tasks.

Accompanying this increased rationality are greater interdependence and greater risk in the performance of jobs. The necessity is greater to understand others' jobs. The errors of others affect one's work more, and errors are more likely to be detected and more likely to be attributable to the person who made them. Equipment can inspect more meticulously than any supervisor or co-worker ever did. These factors, together with the fact that more of the work pace is set by the total integrated system of people and machine, result in employees saying performance standards are tighter and more rigidly enforced, and deadlines more important after a change-over to EDP. In this sense, there is not much question that work in the office has become more like work on the assembly line. In spite of the fact that the workers in these integrated new paper-processing systems see their work as more important, giving them greater opportunities to develop and learn, and more job responsibility, they do not like their jobs more.

2. *Automation in the office increases the volume of work that can be done with a work force, causes extensive reassignments of personnel, but has led directly to few layoffs.* The initial installations of EDP equipment in large corporations do not appear to have resulted in any significant number of layoffs. Transfers and reassignments are the immediate effects; a shrinkage in the need for clerical workers, the more long-run effect. The principal problem here may still turn out to be "the problem of the unhired employee."

A Bureau of Labor Statistics study[8] of experiences of 20 electronic installations provides us with some concrete facts about the extent of

---

[8] Weinberg, E. "Experiences with the Introduction of Office Automation." *Monthly Labor Review*, 1960, 83, 376-380, and U.S. Department of Labor, Bureau of Labor Statistics. *Adjustments to the Introduction of Office Automation.* BLS Report No. 137, Washington, D.C.: U.S. Government Printing Office, 1960.

displacement and reassignments. One-third of the workers in units affected by these early installations had to be reassigned, but only 9 out of 2800 persons were found to have been laid off.

This is a remarkable finding. It indicates the extent to which large companies adopting office automation can provide special "shock absorbers" for their own work force of permanent employees. We have seen that (1) large EDP installations take an average of three years to complete; (2) EDP has its maximum numerical impact on the lower skill level jobs occupied by young women for whom the turnover rate is relatively high; and (3) there have been few problems of retraining employees reassigned in an organization. In these circumstances, it is not surprising to find large companies promising employment security and even no loss in pay to permanent employees. A key question is whether companies can continue such security of employment policies after the initial EDP installations are completed and the extension of EDP to the other possible applications within the organization gets well under way.

How sensitive employees in the office are to these problems of potential technological unemployment appears to vary directly with the size of computer conversion their organization has experienced. In the Michigan State studies of conversions to small computers, it was found that the employees realized machines were replacing workers in some situations, but they did not feel their jobs were threatened. Significantly more employees were worried about temporary layoffs than losing their jobs, in spite of management's assurances of employment security in the change to a large EDP system studied by Mann and Williams.

Now after a decade of explosive growth in the use of computers, there is no question that white collar employees are more aware of the threat to employment. In the past they may have seen this as something the less fortunate blue collar worker had to prepare for and accept when it came; they now keep their company's policy statement assuring no loss of employment because of technological change carefully filed where they can get it at a moment's notice. During the height of the standard turmoil of a conversion to a large computer, they may think about whether a union would not be useful to protect their rights. While from her study of 20 installations in the San Francisco area, Ida Hoos feels that technological change in the office may alter white collar workers' posture toward unionization, there is little objective evidence that organizing drives are encountering any more success than in pre-computer days.

3. *Extensive changes in the division of labor in the office affect both social relations among workers and career patterns.* After a change-over to an electronic computer system, few employees where the machine was placed can say that they are doing the same job, with the same employee work group, under the same supervisor, in the same department. The

transfer of functions and employees involves the breaking up of friendship patterns, and the loss of social anchorages. The more rationalized work process has also resulted in employees working under tighter time schedules and closer monitoring by an integrated system that checks and rechecks. This has resulted in more demanding work. Supervisors, like employees, feel they are under more pressure. Their opinions are solicited less by their superiors; they in turn discuss problems less frequently with their subordinates.

As in the plants, changes in the office alter channels of promotion markedly. There are substantially fewer jobs at both higher and lower skill levels. The reduction in the number of the higher classes means less opportunity for progression. This may eventually undermine some of the white collar worker's illusion of mobility.

4. Automation in the office means higher pay for a few, but essentially the same pay for most employees. In general, the people who become systems analysts and programmers derive the greater financial benefits from the changes. In spite of extensive changes in job content for most clerical employees, the introduction of EDP has raised the average grade of office occupations only slightly.

Employees' satisfaction with their wages after a change-over and a re-evaluation of jobs can be affected negatively by the expectations that they and their supervisors built earlier during the conversion. The new classes of jobs—programmers and electronic equipment operators—are seen as clearly more complex, their own work they knew was harder—especially when they were investing more of themselves for weeks to learn the new tasks. Even their supervisors hope for higher level grades for their employees so their own grades will be higher. When job grades are finally determined, there is often a good deal of questioning about whether the new grades actually reflected the demands of the new jobs.

A word needs to be said about the psychological rewards. In the automated office, as in the automated plant, workers take pride in working on the newest technological acquisition of the organization. In making the physical alterations for housing and air-conditioning the area in which the battery of EDP equipment will be placed, it is not uncommon to replace walls with massive plate glass windows so that the area becomes both literally and figuratively a show-case for visitors.

5. Office automation leads to additional shifts. The frequency with which we see second and third shifts being organized for the operation of computers around the clock is an important new development in the office.

In most organizations the penetration of the computer has been relatively restricted so far, and the continuing rapid development of the capacity of data processing equipment to handle information has forestalled the initiation of additional shifts. It seems probable that, as penetration increases and equipment costs or rentals continue to mount

with increasingly larger built-in capacity, more white collar workers will
be asked, like the blue collar workers before them, to make the personal
and social adjustments necessary to keep the equipment going around
the clock.

SUMMARY OF FINDINGS

*1. Work in the plant and the office is becoming more alike with in-
creasing automation.* Technological changes are forcing changes in the
division of labor, and therefore the content of jobs, in both industrial
plants and offices. The work of employees is generally more important and
their responsibility greater in the most highly automated systems. The
jobs themselves are more demanding, rates of production are higher, an
error or a breakdown in the system more costly. In both situations there
seem to be increased feelings of pressure and tension.

Findings suggest that—at least in the period immediately after the
new equipment begins to function—these jobs provide more challenge,
increased opportunities to learn, and greater variety than jobs under less
advanced technology. One important difference between the factory and
the office is that while the blue collar worker is frequently being asked
to perform a wider range of duties, the predominant trend for the white
collar worker is the opposite.

It would appear that the work satisfaction of both blue collar and
white collar employees has changed very little. If any changes have occurred, blue collar workers are more satisfied while white collar workers
are less satisfied with the new work environments. The forces which
make the jobs in the factory more like office jobs are also making the
office jobs more like the factory jobs.

*2. Workers in both the plant and the office are increasingly aware of
how technological changes affect their lives.* Blue collar workers have
long known that technological change introduces uncertainty into their
world. The relatively stable work world of the white collar worker has
been jarred solidly by the new computer technology. Job displacement
or layoffs are things about which more of them now worry.

Major changes in the organization of work in both the plant and the
office result in major changes in the social relationships among workers
on the job. Formal and informal patterns of interaction and friendship
are broken into by any major change. While there is greater functional
interdependence, the pace of the production process and the responsibilities of continuously maintaining that process serve to restrict contacts and talk to work-relevant topics.

Changes in the job structure alter channels of promotions markedly
in both the plant and the office. Lines of expected progression are wiped

out along with investments of time and experience toward the next step. With smaller work forces and fewer supervisory openings, opportunities for advancement are reduced sharply.

Advances in automation and integrated process equipment which require larger and larger fixed capital investments lead toward multiple-shift operations in both the factory and the office. In a very real sense the requirement that the worker and his family learn to adjust their pattern of living to shift work represents the ultimate in the demand that man adapt to a machine environment.

3. *Major technological change means extended periods of disruption in the basic patterns of working for both blue and white collar workers.* For some individuals this is a period of challenge, excitement, and growth, for others it is a period of vulnerability and emotional turmoil.

A group of bold field experiments[9] showed that when individuals are working at tasks that are highly patterned, requiring little concentration, attention, or thought, neither a series of negative, irritating events nor a series of positive, pleasing events will alter significantly the production of the group. However, when changes in working procedures are introduced, the workers who had been made dissatisfied had more difficulty making the transition than those workers who were relatively undisturbed. These experiments around the introduction of new work procedures indicate a great deal about the general state of readiness that an organization and its members ought to be brought to before a technological change is introduced. But they also suggest how well-mastered and highly predictable patterns of work help protect the individual from what otherwise might be emotionally disrupting phenomena. Predictable patterns of working and relating to others on the job are like gyroscopes in providing the equilibrium that allows many individuals to continue to function effectively.

Man is highly ambivalent about change. Change and variety in life are highly prized, but so are predictability and continuity. There is no simple relationship between change and our liking for change: we can have too much of it or too little. Perhaps what is most disturbing psychologically and socially about the technological changes we are now confronted with is what we sense to be the extended nature of these changes and a seemingly unending and accelerating rate of change. We suspect that change is both functional and dysfunctional for the individual and for the society. What the optimum rate for each of these is we do not know.

[9] S. Schachter, B. Willerman, L. Festinger, R. Hyman, "Emotional Disruption and Industrial Productivity." *Journal of Applied Psychology*, 45 (4), 1961.

Melvin Anshen

4

Managerial Decisions

Recent advances in production technology—popularly identified as automation—have stimulated questions about the future of management organization and the administrative process. Traditional organizations and processes were developed in a very different technology. Will they be effective in a world of continuous-process plants operating under predetermined decision rules? Or will the new technology encourage, perhaps even compel, the design of new management structures and techniques? If so, what are the organizational requirements? What changes in administrative arrangements should be anticipated? What are the implications of these changes for the education, selection, training, and development of managers?

A new production technology in the form of automated processing of materials will not lead to radically new forms of management organization. The principal reason for this is that the way in which work is done on materials does not determine the decisive functions of management. Organization structure and administrative process—which define management hierarchy, relationships, and performance—are largely a response to the requirements of decision-making and decision implementation, not to those of manufacturing technology. The requirements of managerial decision-making in an automated refinery, engine plant, or steel mill are not significantly different in kind (although many times greater in magnitude) from those in an eighteenth-century pottery plant or a nineteenth-century textile mill.

Melvin Anshen *is Professor of Industrial Administration at Carnegie Institute of Technology. During World War II he was director of research for the War Production Board. Author of several books (including* Modern Marketing, *and* Private Enterprise and Public Policy), *Professor Anshen is consultant to corporations on management problems and to the Department of Defense and the Office of Emergency Planning on problems of public administration.*

If we focus on decision-making as a critical characteristic of the management job, however, we can identify one aspect of recent technological advance that is already leading to changes and may lead to more striking ones in the years ahead. The raw material of decision-making is information. And a revolution is under way in information technology: the invention of new quantitative techniques, and new applications for old ones. The computer—an extraordinarily high-powered abacus or a thinking machine—is essential for applying some of these techniques, although no more than handy for others, and even unnecessary for some. The major concern of this chapter, therefore, will be with (1) the character of the new information technology, centering in its well-publicized tool, the computer; and (2) the ways in which technological change in this area may influence organization structure, administration and managers.

STRATEGIC FACTORS IN ADMINISTRATION

The central task of management is to direct the use of resources—physical, financial, and human—in order to achieve defined objectives. In private business the target is profit. In public business and in non-profit organizations there are other targets. But in each situation there is a comparable management responsibility for directing resources.

Elements of decision-making

When management is using resources to attain goals, what does it do? It carries on two related sorts of activities: (1) makes decisions about resources, and (2) implements those decisions. It decides to invest money to acquire materials, machines, and people to build a plant of a determined size and embodying a determined technology, ready for operation at a determined time and place, to bring out a determined product at a determined rate. Having made this set of decisions, it executes them. The plant constructed and working, management runs it. This requires repetitive decisions about rates of production and employment, and about inventory levels in relation to market demand. From time to time technological developments require decisions about new machinery or new materials. Developments in market demand or in the actions of competitors compel decisions bearing on product design or price. Once made, these have to be implemented.

The elements of this job in an organization the size of General Motors are not much different from those in a brick making plant on the banks of the Nile at the time of Moses. In a small and simple situation, the decisions are made by one man, who also takes responsibility for their implementation. In a large and complex situation, many managers are required. As Adam Smith observed in 1776 with respect to the production of pins, large-scale operations create opportunities for gains in efficiency through specialization in detailed parts of a single activity—and similar opportunities are presented for specialization in the decision-making function. To get the benefits of specialization without confusion, it is necessary to design organizational relationships in decision-making, define the limits of responsibility for the component parts, and lay down criteria for performance.

Neither the scale nor the process of production has significant definitional relevance for the tasks of management. A fully automated plant composed of programmed machines running without human direction or intervention would reduce the work of the personnel manager with respect to factory labor. But it would extend his job with respect to the recruitment and administration of technical people.

To understand the process of management, however, we must go one step further. We must answer the question: what is involved in making decisions? A generally acceptable description of the process would identify three successive steps: first, finding occasions for making a decision; second, identifying alternative possible courses of action; third, choosing among the alternatives. While differing in impact at successive levels in the hierarchy, these are the elements of the decision process for the corporation president and for the first-line supervisor.

The role of information

The raw material for decision-making is information. The quality of both information and the processing of it determines the quality of the decisions. By quality of information we mean such factors as relevance, precision, completeness, timeliness. By the quality of information processing we mean such factors as accuracy, speed, ability to handle complex relationships, flexibility, potential for codification in standard rules. We are also concerned with such human characteristics as courage, imagination, and determination. But these are beyond the scope of this analysis.

Rational organization structure is the product of deliberate design that creates a hierarchy of authority and responsibility related at every level to the task of processing information in order to make and execute decisions. The *vertically-peaked structure* funnels information to the higher levels. In organizations of this type most decisions are made by top management, and delegation of decision-making is practiced only for routine problems. Decision-making is placed where the maximum amount of information can be fed to those who possess maximum experience, competence, and responsibility.

This concentration of power may be accompanied by substantial operating disadvantages. Since information has to move along extended reporting channels, decision-making may be slow. Since the deciders are deprived of direct contact with operating problems at their origins, decision-making may be inflexible, marked by the absence of subtle and dynamic response to unique problems.

The flat or horizontal structure requires much decision-making at lower levels, close to the operating problems. This facilitates quick response and flexible adjustment to dynamic and novel situations. These gains may, of course, be accompanied by lower quality of performance resulting from the placement of responsibility in the hands of managers of limited experience and competence, or with a narrow view of the interests of the business as a whole and the complex interrelations of its parts.

Organization structures are not designed solely for making decisions. Managers also carry them out. Good organizations take into consideration the special requirements of implementation. We should also recognize that not all organization designs are good with respect to either decision-making or decision execution. But the use of information for decision-making must be a formative influence in effective design of structure and process.

Types of decisions

It will be useful to distinguish between two broad categories of decisions. In the language of computers, we can think of *programmed* decisions and *nonprogrammed* decisions—convenient labels for the extremes of what is in reality a continuum.

Programmed decisions are routine and repetitive; those who make them can follow tested rules. Routine inventory replacement of standard operating supplies, routine pricing of orders, routine treatment of employee absences—these are familiar examples.

In contrast, *nonprogrammed decisions* are novel and complex, demanding special treatment. General Eisenhower's D-Day decision is a classic example. Examples in business would be decisions to add or drop a product, to make a fundamental change in financial structure, to undertake a major commitment in research and development, to introduce an innovation in collective bargaining (such as the American Motors contract with the United Auto Workers in 1961). In most nonprogrammed decisions, of course, some components are programmed, as was the case with the logistics of the D-Day undertaking.

Different information-processing and decision-making techniques are used in dealing with the programmed and nonprogrammed categories. The differences have significance for understanding the impact of the new information-processing technology on organization structure and administrative process. The impact is not likely to be the same all along the continuum of decision-making techniques. The resulting changes in structure and process will therefore be markedly diverse at remote points along the continuum.

THE NEW INFORMATION TECHNOLOGY

The new information technology enters the world of management in two ways. The first is marked by the use of powerful computers in processing masses of data previously handled by clerks using pencil calculations and simple machines with slow speed and limited capacity. The second is marked by the application of sophisticated techniques of quantitative analysis, both old and new, to management problems. The joint impact is novel and massive enough to deserve its common description as a revolution in the technology of business administration. Indeed, some have declared that it constitutes a radical transformation in management equal in magnitude and significance to the changes in production methods brought about by the Industrial Revolution.

The automated abacus

While the more interesting and important aspects of this revolution are connected with the new analytic techniques, it is the computer as a high-speed automated abacus that has captured the popular imagination. The machine that will replace many clerks resembles the machine that will replace production workers. Actually, this view is too simple. It fails to grasp the meaning of the displacement for organization structure and management. The clerks were processing information for decision-making, and their displacement by high-powered machines makes possible gross multiplication of the scale of calculation and physical transfer of the place of calculation, accompanied by startling reductions in time. The net result can be, for example, a transfer of information processing from decentralized locations to headquarters, with net gains in speed and accuracy. Where this can be done, important changes in organization structure and process may follow. For example, a company that previously decentralized its administration in order to put decision-making close to the source of information will now be in a position to bring decision-making back to headquarters where information can be processed faster and better. And this is exactly what some companies have begun to do with scattered manufacturing plants.

New analytic techniques

The new analytic techniques for processing information have developed primarily from the initial impetus during World War II when military problems engaged the attention of large numbers of mathematicians, statisticians, mathematical economists, and other scientists. Popularly known as operations research or management science, the approaches devised then and in the following years have brought an array of quantitative techniques to bear on a wide range of management problems, including many that had never before appeared susceptible to analysis and rational resolution.

Among these analytic techniques we can identify the following:

Linear Programming—using a mathematical formulation (such as a set of equations) for obtaining the theoretically best solution for problems of allocation of scarce resources among competing uses. Linear programming has been used, for example, in the mixing of commercial cattle feeds and in the operation of a petroleum refinery.

Dynamic Programming—a mathematical formulation applicable to the problems of economic administration of continuous, interrelated processes, such as those encountered in multi-stage inventories (moving goods through factory-field-wholesale-retail inventory holding points) or production scheduling through sequential departments.

Game Theory—introducing into mathematical formulation considerations of strategy and counter-strategy among competitors, to find the best strategy against an opponent's possible actions. Such formulations have been used in marketing operations where brand, price, and comparable decisions desirably should be made only after consideration of actions open to competitors.

Statistical Decision Theory—for introducing subjective assessments of probability into mathematical formulations of management problems. One example would be in the consideration of alternative possible investments of a fund of capital, where each investment under analysis reveals a different potential pay-back accompanied by an estimated probability of securing that pay-back.

Heuristic Programming—a computer technique utilizing shortcuts in the form of "rules of thumb" or "heuristics" which greatly reduces the volume of computations involved in solving a complex problem. Among other applications, heuristic programming has been used in solving scheduling problems in job-shop manufacturing.

Whatever their character, these tools of analysis share certain fundamental operating characteristics. First, they require the construction of a set of mathematical equations that reflect the relationships among the important variables in a problem requiring management decision. These variables might, for example, include costs at various scales of operation, changes in scale in relation to time, profits, etc. In effect, this is no more than a translation into precise mathematical terms of a description of the elements in a problem confronting a manager and the relationships among these variables as changes in one variable influence changes in other variables. Such a mathematical formulation is commonly referred to among the technicians of information processing as a "model."

The second requirement is the selection of a measure for choosing among various possible alternative courses of action. This might mean, in a production scheduling problem, choosing that production schedule which will minimize total production costs—or in another production scheduling problem, choosing that schedule which will minimize fluctuations in plant employment. In a marketing setting, this might mean choosing that pattern of distribution from field warehouses which will minimize transportation costs in handling all orders. Information technicians commonly refer to this as the selection of a criterion function, which is no more than identifying the measure by which the attractiveness of competing alternatives will be assessed.

The third requirement is the ability to replace the algebraic symbols in the equations with numbers. This involves using records, experience, and judgment to quantify every variable in the model. At this stage the "x" and "y" of high-school algebra are replaced by numbers. Since accounting, financial, and operating records are not always maintained in a form that will readily yield such numbers for all variables, it is sometimes necessary to retreat to the judgment and informed guesses of managers. For example, in dealing with the problem of determining the optimum inventory to hold in order to secure the most profitable compromise between the desire to satisfy all customers' orders promptly and the desire to minimize inventory investment and holding costs, it may be necessary to estimate the cost of not filling a customer's order promptly, which may mean a lost order.

The final requirement is the solution of the set of related equations. Given the quantitative estimates fitted into the equations, this will identify the solution that will maximize the chosen standard measure or criterion function. All this implies no more than designing a rule for making a decision in a particular problem situation. In computer language, this is a "program."

A practical problem in current application involves using such a mathematical model, expressed as a program for a computer, for making periodic decisions about raw material mix for commercial animal feed. Here, various materials can be combined in various proportions to yield feed with certain desired characteristics. Shifting material costs create a complex problem that used to be resolved by rough hand calculation and human judgment. One feed company today has turned the problem over to a suitably directed computer which employs a mathematically-determined program to generate optimum decisions related to each shifting network of costs and proportional mixes.

Electronic computers enter as instruments for making the large number of calculations involved in solving the equations that are the common expression of the models of system relationships. In many of these applications computers have greatly extended the possibility of applying mathematical techniques to management problems requiring calculations far beyond the capacity of older and less powerful tools. These analytic applications of the computer can be combined with more routine applications of a data-processing character. The result is a new information technology whose impact on traditional organization structure and administrative process is now an object of intensive study and often substantial disagreement.

REVOLUTION OR EVOLUTION?

Will the new information technology revolutionize the decision-making process and thereby bring about radical changes in organization structure and administration? The question has generated diverse answers. Some writers—foreseeing full-scale revolution—have predicted such changes as:

1. An upward shift of the boundary between planning and performance, as a result of which many planning responsibilities will be removed from middle-level managers.

2. A reversal of the recent trend toward decentralized operations, with top management taking on a much larger share of the innovating, planning, and creating functions.

3. Radical reorganization of middle management structure, downgrading the status of some jobs and upgrading others.

4. The appearance of a sharper, more impenetrable demarcation between the top and the middle of the organizational structure. Those who hold these views (advanced with vigor by Leavitt and Whisler in "Management in the 1980's," *Harvard Business Review*) clearly believe that the managerial function ultimately will be influenced along its full range. If this is right, the structures of business organizations and the jobs of managers will see revolutionary changes indeed.

Constraints

Others argue that a forecast of this character is open to challenge on at least three grounds.

First, the projection rests on the assumption that within the fore-seeable future analytic techniques based on computers will be capable of handling almost the entire range of decisions made by managers, in-cluding a large share of the nonprogrammed category. Many, including this writer, would counter that while the computer's "black box" will in time be capable of doing most types of programmed decision-making, the capacity to make nonprogrammed decisions will be acquired slowly and will be limited for a long time to come.

Second, the projection appears not to recognize economic constraints on computers. As Herbert A. Simon has observed in *The New Science of Management Decision*:

> If I am right in my optimistic prediction that we are rapidly dissolving the mysteries that surround nonprogrammed decision-making, then the question of how far that decision-making shall be automated ceases to be a technological question and becomes an economic question. Technologically, it is today feasible to get all our energy directly from the sun. . . . Economically, of course, it is not feasible at all. The capital investment required for direct conversion of the sun's rays to heat is so large that only in a few desert climates is the process even marginally efficient.
>
> Similarly, the fact that a computer can do something a man can do does not mean that we will employ the computer instead of the man. Computers are today demonstrably more economical than men for most large-scale arith-metic computations. In most business data-processing tasks they are some-where near the break-even point—whether they can prove themselves in terms of costs depends on the volume of work and on the biases of the man who makes the calculations. . . .
>
> To put the matter crudely, if a computer rents for $10,000 a month, we cannot afford to use it for nonprogrammed decision-making unless its output of such decisions is equivalent to that of ten men at middle-management levels. Our experience to date—which is admittedly slight—suggests that com-puters do not have anything like the comparative advantage in efficiency over humans in the area of heuristic problem solving that they have in arithmetic and scientific computing.

Third, the projection gives scant attention to the problems of man-machine relationships created by the introduction of a partially com-puterized decision technology within an organization of human managers. Most of the enthusiastic literature of mechanized and automated decision-making flatly ignores this complex relationship. Technicians see oppor-tunities for applying their skills. They develop rules, programs, and auto-mated procedures for making better decisions than managers can make on the basis of crude experience and rough rules of thumb. The new technology is sold to management and installed. Then the inventors turn their attention to other problems.

Relatively little study has been devoted to what happens after the installation. But at least a few case histories suggest that results do not always proceed as anticipated. Problems that have been analyzed solely in terms of information processing are often complicated by other factors, such as individual and group motivations, pressures, and goal divergencies. The influence of these factors may persist—often in exacerbated form. These experiences urge adoption of a larger frame of reference than most technical specialists are inclined to use, a recognition of the human and functional interplay. To the extent that this view gains acceptance, the introduction of automated information processing is likely to be slowed and moderated as managers attain a more perceptive understanding of the intricate problems of man-machine relationships.

Locating the impact

Most of the growing volume of applications of automated decision-making involve programmed decisions. They include applications to process, batch, and item scheduling in production; inventory, shipment, and transportation scheduling in distribution; and capital budgeting in finance. These problems possess common characteristics that make them susceptible to automated solutions. The principal variables in each situation are usually quantified in existing accounting, cost, and financial record systems—or can be quantified by reasonable estimates based on existing records and experienced judgment. The problems involve the efficient use of scarce resources subject to identifiable constraints, and a specific criterion function can be selected (maximize profits, minimize costs, etc.). Repetitive decisions are required over a period of time. The principal decision elements are constant in the repetitive decisions. As a result, the typical decision situation is composed of identified, articulated, and quantified elements capable of being manipulated in a rigorous manner.

Consider, by way of contrast, some typical examples of nonprogrammed decisions:

One group of decisions is concerned with finding problems that need to be solved and assigning priorities to them. Recognition of inadequacies in a distribution system, and initiating steps to remove them; determining that maintenance of a healthy competitive position requires expansion in scale of operations, and initiating plans for defining and securing the necessary funds; discovering that inventories have accumulated to undesirable levels, and launching studies to accomplish reduction without impairing customer service; concluding that a decentralization program places unusual demands on lower-level managers, and mobilizing educational and developmental activities to improve their ability to handle novel responsibilities—these are all examples of what may be called agenda problems.

Another group of decisions is concerned with selecting specific targets for accomplishment by the organization as a whole or its component parts. Examples would include: setting sales or profit objectives, defining time horizons for the accomplishment of identified projects such as broadening product lines, and determining targets of achievement for a public relations program. These may be conveniently termed *goal choice decisions.*

Still another group of decisions is involved with questions of implementation: what decisions can be executed most economically in view of available resources, time, and experience; how to get accomplishment through people; how to encourage innovation in a conservative organizational environment.

In all these classes of decisions we see nonprogrammed elements. Many of the relevant variables are unknown or uncertain. The possibility of quantifying such variables as can be identified is limited. Solution of the problems calls for truly creative thinking. A good part of almost every problem revolves around the issue of what to think *about,* in contrast to the question of how to reach an answer when the problem elements are known and their relationships are defined or definable in quantitative terms.

The thrust of the new information-processing technology has been toward the structured, programmed area and is likely to remain there for some time to come. With unstructured, nonprogrammed problems, management science will probably make only limited progress. Since many of these problems are of central importance, both the scope and the speed of change in organization structure and administrative process will be considerably less than some enthusiasts of the new technology have predicted. This is not a denial of the significance of the changes that lie ahead and, indeed, have already begun to be accomplished. Rather, it suggests the importance of making prediction much more specific with respect to the area and direction of changes in the performance of the management function. What we are concerned with is much more evolutionary than revolutionary. This is a distinction that puts a premium on accurate prediction, since anticipation of change can lead to more intelligent administration of the innovation process itself.

CHANGING CONTENT OF THE MANAGER'S JOB

Will the automated decision displace human managers? At least in the area of programmed decisions, characteristically encountered in middle management, will computers take over the principal functions of managers?

Opportunities to enrich the job

Predictable gains in automated information-processing will bring about a substantial transfer of responsibility for making programmed decisions from managers to machines. However, this need not lead to a withering away of middle management. Rather, automation will open new opportunities for more effective performance of the decision implementation functions that often are scanted or handled within an unduly narrow context. Beyond this, it opens the possibility of bringing about a more imaginative attack on those aspects of management performance with which many top-level executives are most dissatisfied—the creative activities of problem identification and decision implementation.

Consider, for example, the case of the manager of a plant engaged in batch processing of several raw materials that can be combined in various ways to yield satisfactory mixtures for further manufacture. In scheduling the material mix and the rate of plant operation, the manager had been concerned with frequent shifts in raw material costs and equally frequent shifts in customer demand and market prices transmitted to him through distributor and plant warehouse buffers, as well as with the labor costs of steady and erratic employment. For many years the plant manager had devoted up to two-thirds of his time to making and supervising the making of this complex of decisions, and to conferring with other managers in finance, accounting, and sales about current and contemplated material mix, product mix, and work scheduling. Then a computer program was developed. After a year's operation under automation, the manager reported that over-all supervision of the computer's performance and administrative discussions bearing on the resulting decisions were claiming only about ten percent of his time. What was he doing with the released hours? Here is his own analysis of how his job had changed:

> First, I now find myself free to take a look at the operation of the plant as a whole, as a system of materials, machines, and people, and to think about how to introduce changes in that system to make the operation more profitable. I did a little of this before—and staff people from headquarters would descend on me from time to time to try to do more of it—but I was always being dragged away by the necessity for meeting decision deadlines, and the rest of the staff lacked the detailed knowledge required for a truly creative attack on the problems. I anticipate being able during the next year to introduce changes that will save my annual salary at least—and I don't think that will be the end of it.
>
> Second, I have more time to spend on personnel problems. We've never had a major labor relations trouble spot here, but we sure have had a series of minor upsets, dissatisfaction with the grievance procedure, cases of inept foremen-worker relations, things of that sort. I didn't know what the fundamental trouble was and never had the time to find out. I am beginning to

dig into the situation now. I am finding out some things I never knew, and some of them are things I can fix. I can sit down now and talk with union leadership from time to time, and on the basis of what I have learned we are going to institute a program of foremen training that should make a big contribution toward smoothing out a lot of the friction.

Third, I've got the time to take an active role in a couple of community projects. I think this will help the company's public relations here in town, and will broaden my own education as a manager in an ever-growing area of management responsibility.

Finally, I can spend more time on understanding relationships with other parts of this business. I've been able to visit a couple of our warehouses and a few of their customers and find out what their problems look like. Ideas from this will make the plant a better supplier. If your question is: 'Have I got idle time on my hands?' the answer is emphatically 'No.' I'm not doing what I used to do. I think I'm doing more important things that never used to get done, or used to get taken care of with a lick and a promise. And my boss thinks so, too.

This example suggests the challenge to top management to think creatively about the introduction of automated decision-making and to resist the temptation to accept the machine as a complete substitute for the information-processing manager. The machine cannot serve this purpose, and it should not be introduced on the assumption that it can. As an aid to management, however, it can make useful contributions.

Opportunities to enlarge the job

Most of the initial thinking about information processing by computer viewed it as a collection of devices for doing rapidly, efficiently, and rationally what managers have been doing slowly, inefficiently, and often only semi-rationally. This view is undesirably limited. Automation also makes possible an enlargement of the total range of decision-making. In fact, this may come to be the most valuable contribution of the new information technology to management practice.

It is now possible for the first time to consider the total activity of a firm—from research and development through production and distribution to financial results—as a single integrated system. Within this system, a dynamic network of relationships can be discerned and measured, with feedback loops and forces for multiplying and dampening the effects of actions at earlier stages in the continuous process. Analytic techniques based on the programmed computer permit managers to simulate the performance of such a system and to test its output under a range of changing variables within and outside the system. This technical advance is only one among many possibilities now available for extending the scope of decision-making.

Such an enlargement of management grasp cannot fail to enrich the executive's job. It has been a commonplace to observe that one of the prime responsibilities of top management has been to consider the operation of the business as a whole and to make decisions within this integrated context. But until the introduction of the new analytic apparatus, it has been difficult for top management to fulfill this responsibility, because the business as a whole is often too complex to understand. Rather than displacing it, therefore, the new technology is bringing under management a new world of decision-making opportunities. Some decisions will ultimately be made by programmed computers, to be sure. But more importantly, this new tool will greatly extend management's creative potential by revealing opportunities for identifying problems that previously were not even known to exist.

AUTOMATION AND MANAGEMENT ORGANIZATION

What conclusions, then, are suggested about the effect of the new technology on management structure and process? In answering this we should remember that we are examining a development whose operation will depend on both technological capability and economic advantage. We should also remember that the tasks of administering the new technology and its attached corps of professionals will themselves present difficulties for top management. On this point, a few final words will be in order on the implications of the new technology for the education, training, and development of managers.

Organization structure and job content

The most significant changes probably will occur in making programmed decisions, principally found at middle and junior levels. It is here that the major thrust of the new technology will be experienced. But the effect will not be to displace managers. Rather, it will be to change their jobs by reducing their routine tasks. This will open opportunities for more creative work in problem identification and more thorough implementation. As these changes occur, the demands on middle managers will grow in complexity and become more like demands placed on top managers. Middle-level management will thereby become a more thorough testing ground for promotion to higher levels.

Since the change projected here is a redefinition of job content and not a removal of job function, there is no reason to anticipate significant innovations in the visible structure of organization hierarchy. Management job descriptions will need substantial rewriting with the passage of time, but the organization charts will not be redrawn. The considerations that lead large organizations to a hierarchical form of relationships will continue to be influential because they will continue to indicate the economic and efficient way of getting the work done. In short, managers will have more tools for making decisions, but managers will not become obsolete.

This projected change in job content will place new demands on middle-level managers, however. To be effective administrators in the new environment they will have to understand computers. They will be called on to work with computer technicians in analyzing the relevant components of the decision process and in designing rules. Some of the implications of these requirements are discussed later.

Trend toward centralization

The marked trend toward decentralization of decision-making in large organizations probably will be slowed and in part reversed. The ability to transmit information rapidly and to accomplish mass data processing economically on centrally-located computers will make it possible and desirable to return to headquarters a share of the decision-making responsibility that has been pushed to regional and district offices or to the managers of product groups. This will certainly occur in those organizations which had decentralized decision-making primarily to place responsibility where the relevant information was generated and could be processed rapidly.

It should be observed, however, that centralized data processing—designed to take advantage of the economics of computer hardware—does not necessarily remove the possibility of returning the computer's output to managers in field locations for their administrative use. This may occur where the central computer is used in automated clerical work, essentially arithmetical in character, rather than in producing decisions in accordance with programmed instructions.

In short, in thinking about automated information processing as an influence on the placement of the decision responsibility, the critical factor is the purpose served by automation. Mechanizing clerical routines creates one situation; mechanizing the decision function creates another. Only in the latter situation will there be any important impact on what managers do and how they do it.

Role of computer technicians

Professional experts in automated data handling will occupy positions of growing importance and will exercise an increasing influence on the whole system of information processing and decision-making. Where the new technology is employed most creatively to extend the range of decision-making capability, they will have a role in recommending the redesign of information flow and the placement of decision responsibility. It is doubtful, however, that technicians will come to assume top-management responsibilities. Perhaps of greater significance, they are not likely to constitute a reservoir from which top-management personnel are drawn. Even highly-developed technical competence does not qualify a man to handle nonprogrammed decisions or to perform skillfully in getting decisions implemented through people.

In assessing the organization role of the professionals in this field, a critical danger should be identified. It is tempting for top management to admit its ignorance about advanced techniques of analysis and the use of computers and to surrender its prerogatives to those with specialized competence. Those organizations in which this error is permitted to occur —and there have been a substantial number—invite a serious risk of distorting and eroding management. Excessive investment in hardware is only one of the mistakes that may follow. At least as dangerous is a public downgrading of the creative functions of managers which not only cannot be replaced by automated information processing but also should be enlarged in scope and increased in importance.

To permit professional specialists in information processing to make the big decisions about the magnitude and timing of the investment in automated decision-making, or about consequent changes in organization structure and administrative process, would be a dangerous abandonment of management responsibility. Professional specialists are no more competent in this area than in any other to commit an organization to fundamental changes in function and performance. Their expert knowledge is valuable, but their judgments are almost inevitably narrow and limited. A good analogy is President Eisenhower's forceful criticism of attempts by professional soldiers to determine the size of the nation's military budget. Just as there is more to federal budget decisions than defense dollars, and more to national security than capacity for nuclear defense and retaliation, so there is more to management than automated information processing and programmed decision-making.

Organizations as systems

The unsophisticated outsider who seeks to discover from a formal organization chart how a firm actually behaves is likely to draw erroneous conclusions about the extent of co-ordination and integration of activities. Because of inherent limitations in the capacity of a decision-making complex to collect, analyze and use large bodies of information in reaching effectively integrated decisions, all large organizations have probably failed by a considerable margin to attain economic coordination of related functions. Directing materials and semi-finished work through successive manufacturing departments is often so complex as to require scheduling operations in each department independently and using buffer stocks between departments to prevent fluctuations in one unit from disrupting operations in a following unit. Even greater disruptions are found in integrating operations between production and distribution.

It is becoming clear that operations research aimed at treating the organization as an integrated system has a potentially high value. Substantial savings should follow the application of decision rules designed to optimize production rates and inventory levels within a unified flow of activity. This possibility will encourage the central location of an enlarged scheduling function close to the top of the organization tree.

The positive gain will be a rational command of resources, realized in efficiency and economy. The positive danger will be a disposition to surrender ultimate administrative responsibility to automated operating behavior. Management will possess a powerful tool. But the human imagination will continue to be a prime contribution to organization success, which can come only through managers who are the masters and not the servants of their new tool.

Education of managers

Managers must acquire a comprehensive and penetrating understanding of the new technology. If they are to make wise investments in computer hardware and wise conclusions about decision-making responsibility, top level executives must know both the capabilities and the limitations of the technology. They must understand the thinking of professionals in this growing field, their approach to operating problems, and their special vocabulary. At middle levels, managers will have to learn to cooperate with operations researchers and computer technicians. They will have to participate in the critical analysis of the information and decision process and in the design of automated procedures for handling programmed decisions.

Knowledge will expand on how to select decisions that can be partially programmed. New analytic techniques will be invented for coping with (1) nonprogrammed decisions that can be at least partially programmed, and (2) nonprogrammed decisions in their own terms. Middle-level managers must therefore be equipped to guide the expanding technology into new areas of activity.

The manager of the 1970's who does not understand the capabilities of automated information-processing techniques will be handicapped. He will run the risk of becoming the servant of the professional experts of the new technology. He will be incapable of bringing rational judgment to bear on proposals for investment in computer hardware. He will not understand how to adapt organization structure and administrative process to the potential of the new tools.

Some graduate schools of administration have already recognized this problem and have taken steps to introduce appropriate work in their curricula. The pressure will grow for others to acquaint their students with the new technology. For the same compelling reason, managers in middle-level positions are well advised to familiarize themselves with the concepts and tools of the new science of management decision.

George W. Taylor

5

Collective Bargaining

Early in his administration, President Kennedy appointed a tripartite Advisory Committee on Labor-Management Policy. Its very first report to the President, submitted on January 11, 1962, dealt with the problems of technological change. The committee unanimously agreed that:

(1) automation and technological progress are essential to the general welfare, the economic strength and the defense of the nation; (2) this progress can and must be achieved without sacrifice of human values; and (3) achievement of technological progress without sacrifice of human values requires a combination of private and governmental action, consonant with the principles of a free society.

The emphasis upon human values makes this a notable statement. It sparks anew the question: What price are we willing to pay for efficiency? This becomes a pertinent question only once it is determined that the machine must serve man's interests. A conservation of the interests of employees directly affected by technological change involves costs that are as much a part of adapting so-called automation to our purposes as the

---

Author of many books on industrial problems, GEORGE W. TAYLOR *is Professor of Industry at the Wharton School of Finance and Commerce, University of Pennsylvania. Dr. Taylor was Vice Chairman and Chairman of the National War Labor Board (1942-45); Chairman of The National Wage Stabilization Board (1951) and of the Presidential Board of Inquiry for the Steel Strike (1959); and member of the President's Advisory Committee on Labor-Management Policy (1961). Over the years he has been impartial Chairman and Arbitrator under numerous labor agreements.*

Dr. Taylor is grateful to Dr. Richard L. Rowan of the Wharton School, University of Pennsylvania, who assisted in the preparation of this chapter.

costs of research and development, building the machine, and "getting the bugs out of it." These additional costs assessed to automation can, at times, be excessive, but this can also be true of every preceding step. And, I feel certain of the rightness of the general principle as a support for democracy as conceived in the Western world.

Let there be no mistake in realizing that conservation of human values as a dimension of technological change is of recent origin. Consider this observation made in a semi-official report issued in 1929: "Whereas workers can be easily added or subtracted, and the employer is not committing himself to any long-time arrangements in employing them, machinery can be less easily adjusted. . . ."[1] Or these congratulatory comments in the same report about the growing unselfishness of business men: ". . . To the organization itself, and to its investors, there is a decided sense of responsibility. Toward customers, also, there is such a sense; at least, *caveat emptor* as an alibi is dead. Toward employees, there is less feeling of responsibility, yet there is some."

Over the intervening years, the economics of labor utilization has been recast. The plight of the individual employee adversely affected by technology has become of considerable concern to unions, employers and the government. And, the right of employees to share in the benefits of higher productivity is widely conceded even though they do not cause the increases by their own efforts. Many new problems about relative rights and equities have been created and the road to accommodation is not yet clearly marked. Nevertheless, in the change of basic principles our society has matured and is in a far better position to assume the role as leader of the democracies.

It is the new set of standards for sharing the benefits of technology with employees which make the present technological adjustment problems different from anything that has gone before. (For example, in the technological revolution of the 1920's, there was a relatively high public tolerance of unemployment and the employee's share in added productivity was widely computed as but a part of the additional output accruing from his working at incentive pace rather than at normal pace. It was reasoned that management was entitled to a share having made the incentive pace possible.)

Because the union is assigned the function of representing the interests of the employees in collective bargaining, it has a vital role in technological change. But, the interests of the employees also include their need for work uninterrupted by strikes and employment by a prosperous company able to provide good, steady jobs. The manner in which the union performs its representational function is an important determinant of economic and social progress.

There are cases, relatively few but still far too numerous, in which a

[1] Conference on Unemployment, "Recent Economic Changes in the United States" (New York: McGraw-Hill Book Co., Inc., 1929), Volume 1, pp. 177-178.

union seeks to gain job security for its members by obstructing mechanization and through make-work devices. They can reflect inadequate union leadership but can also be a forthright representation of the will of employees. These are instances of collective bargaining failure and are, fortunately, in the minority. Collective bargaining is generally conceived and used by unions as the best method to determine the employees' share of the benefits of mechanization, to ameliorate the impact of employee displacement, and to promulgate rules governing the manning and operation of equipment. These involve costs to the employer which are sometimes hard to absorb either out of profits or through price increases.

It is about the degree of such cost increases that the impasses in collective bargaining arise and public concern over price increases is aroused. Do excessive costs accrue because of an over-emphasis, under collective bargaining, of the rights of those employees who are affected by technological change? That is, are valid rights being protected or unwarranted privileges being granted? Do such costs unduly aggravate inflationary forces? Are work rules essentially of the featherbedding variety and do they, therefore, interfere unreasonably with the attainment of the high production and high productivity necessary for national welfare and safety? These questions, and others of a similar nature, have swelled into a national debate in which collective bargaining is on trial.

Evidence to support affirmative answers to each of the questions raised above can be adduced by pointing to particular cases. They are not hard to find. For example; the success of a union in guarding its members against an automation, anticipated to come at some indeterminate time in the future, through a provision for an immediate 25-hour week, with additional hours guaranteed at overtime rates, might seem to be preferential treatment for the employees. Especially is this the case when the present job opportunities far exceed the number of available employees. Other kinds of evidence can be referred to. The tendency of wage-rate increases to exceed productivity increases, in recent years, raises doubts about the equity of the share in productivity conceded to the employer for dividends and for plant expansion and to the consumer who pays the prices. There are also plenty of obsolete work rules around. I have witnessed a form of "simultaneous seniority," for example, in which the assignment of men to jobs was more like a day-long game of musical chairs than a support of purposeful productive operations.

There is considerable evidence, then, of excess union bargaining power. This is not particularly typical of those industry-wide situations where only the union has a "power to shut down the whole industry." Indeed, the more convincing evidence is found in many local bargaining situations which are less spectacular or even anonymous as far as the public is concerned. Despite this evidence, the thesis here advanced is that, on balance, collective bargaining has been, and is, quite an effective method of facilitating technological change in a constructive manner under today's standards. It is asserted that no better alternative means are available. Moreover, while granting that many of the concomitant problems of automation, such as the unemployment of displaced workers, cannot be grappled with exclusively by collective bargaining, the most critical ones can best be so resolved. The evidence of shortcomings does suggest, nevertheless, that institutional changes designed to adapt collective bargaining to the exacting environment of the mid-twentieth century have become urgently necessary.

The fundamental reason for the views just expressed is the essentiality, in a free democratic country, of an agreement-making mechanism capable of creating a high degree of acceptance of employment terms by those employees and the management directly affected by technological change. Collective bargaining is counted upon to consummate the agreements upon which we depend. In a sense, our institutions designed to assist accommodation and to provide agreements provide the democratic antidote to the Marxian dialectic process. Our view of "labor" is quite different from that of the totalitarians.

LABOR AS A FACTOR OF PRODUCTION

As a factor of production, labor has unique characteristics. It is not inanimate like the others—machines, buildings, raw material and the like. Special rules regarding both the payments for labor services and the manner of labor utilization have accordingly been established by law and by private contract. Moreover, the productive output of labor is a variable depending upon personal motivation, including the acceptability of employment terms. This is especially true of free labor.

In collective bargaining a reconciliation of the needs of employee and employer has to be effected. The resulting labor cost can only be estimated and not precisely calculated by management. Employees also face uncertainties. With few exceptions, they cannot be sure of full employment or, indeed, of any employment at all. The labor contract has to be consummated, then, in terms of forecasts of the future.

Under these conditions, the bargaining environment of the 1960's is unusually exacting. Union and management leaders have never been assigned more difficult roles than those now requiring them to balance and mediate between various intense pressures—for lower costs, for higher and uninterrupted production, for job security, for other protection of the interests of those employees who contribute to, and are affected by, technological change, and restraint in the public interest. The equation is so complex that a substitution of analytical processes for economic power bargaining has to be made if constructive decisions are to be evolved. As will be noted presently, institutional changes are important in this connection.

Nevertheless, the objective of collective bargaining remains the discovery of employment terms which will be accepted by those directly affected—employees and management alike. The agreement is construed as giving such terms a rightness not otherwise achievable and as a means of evoking those personal efforts which give high productivity. There can be no doubt that what employees produce in that hour for which each receives a stated wage is quite a variable. The output depends, in no small measure, upon employee appraisal of the fairness and equity of terms of employment but, as importantly, upon the acceptability of conditions of employment, including work rules. Low wages and rigid rules can result in high labor costs, and frequently do.

Differences in the tempo and purposefulness of work between comparable plants in the same industry stand out sharply to those of us who frequently go through factories. The resulting variations in labor cost at the same hourly rate, I estimate, are frequently as much as 25 percent and sometimes more. To ignore this factor is to construct a doubtful abstraction for reasoning about labor cost behavior. By providing a direct representation for employees in fixing the terms of employment and in gaining their assent to the terms, collective bargaining is conceived as an aid to increased production. Sometimes, of course, the contrary results obtain. Collective bargaining is not a self-effectuating mechanism.

One may well ponder why so-called institutionalism is so often made relatively subordinate in current economic analysis despite the fact that institutional forms are designed to carry out some of the most vital value judgments which society makes. Institutionalism thus has its own logic though not akin to that followed in much model building, so fashionable nowadays, in which top priority is assigned to selected goals while other factors are excluded. In analyzing production and productivity, the elusive "employee morale" aspect is not of lesser importance because it cannot be easily quantified.

Collective bargaining conserves, then, what is termed voluntarism in labor relations. This is essential to the orderly and productive effectuation of technological change. Adherence to the principle is difficult in view of the stepped-up expectations of collective bargaining. Yet, there are demonstrated strengths of this process which should not be entirely obscured by a concentration upon broad national problems.

Union Policies and Technological Change

Within the limits imposed by their representational function, unions have generally accepted a form of "high wage—low labor cost" doctrine. This has long been, and still is, a notable characteristic of the American economic scene. Almost without exception, union leaders recognize that increased productivity per man hour, arising from mechanization, is the key to easier jobs and improved living standards for employees.

Reference to two instances in which this point of view has been made particularly explicit in labor agreements seems appropriate. The groundbreaking 1948 and 1950 Agreements between General Motors Corporation and the United Automobile Workers of America provided for annual productivity wage increases. Article 101 (a) of the 1950 Agreement stated a principle important to the parties but rather lost sight of in the continuing argument about the soundness of this kind of employee sharing in productivity gains. It reads:

> The annual improvement factor provided herein recognizes that a continuing improvement in the standard of living of employees depends upon technological progress, better tools, methods, processes and equipment and a co-operative attitude on the part of all parties in such progress. It further recognizes the principle that to produce more with the same amount of human effort is a sound economic and social objective.

On this basis, negotiations have been constructively carried out with a minimum of interruption to production and without governmental intervention.

Great interest has been aroused by a more recent undertaking. In the face of a drastic impairment of their members' job security, because of improved machinery and methods, the Amalgamated Meat Cutters and Butcher Workmen of North America and the United Packinghouse Workers of America agreed with Armour and Company on a policy toward technological change. This was enunciated in Appendix 1 of the August 31, 1959 Agreement. It reads:

> . . . the meat packing industry is undergoing significant changes in methods of production, processing, marketing and distribution. Armours' modernization program is vital to its ability to compete and grow successfully, thus providing a reasonable return on capital invested in the enterprise and providing the assurance of continued employment for the employees under fair standards of wages, benefits and working conditions.

That Agreement went further. The company recognized that

> . . . mechanization and new methods to promote operating and distributing efficiencies affect the number of employees required and the manner in which they perform their work . . . these problems require continued study to promote employment opportunities for employees affected by the introduction of more efficient methods and technological changes.

Novel steps were taken to carry out these general principles. Although the results fell considerably short of initial hopes, they afford invaluable experience for the guidance not only of the meat-packing industry but more generally for dealing with the displacement of semi-skilled workers.

There are other cases in which the salutary results of union co-operation in technological change is evident in the statistics. The bituminous coal industry is a notable example. The United Mine Workers of America has, for many years, actively encouraged the modernization of mining operations. That made possible substantial gains in wage rates, hours, and working conditions for those who kept their jobs. Employment opportunities in the industry declined sharply but that brought advantages as well as disadvantages. From one point of view, the principal conservation of human values was in making it possible for the industry to meet society's demand for coal by exposing only 150,000 men instead of 500,000 to the harsh dangers of mining.

Substitution of machines for men is an old story in the bituminous coal industry. Since 1948, however, mechanization brought about an unprecedented transformation. It has been estimated that, in constant dollars, the net value of plant and equipment per worker in the industry increased at an annual rate of 10 percent from 1948 to 1959. In consequence, within a decade, output per production worker man-hour increased by 85 percent or at an annual rate of 6.4 percent. Improvement rates were but slightly less for all employee man-hours including those worked in the offices. The number of production workers fell by three-fifths or to less than 150,000 employees while total production remained about the same. Only to a relatively limited extent, through industry welfare funds, did the displaced people share in the industry's technological gains. Their continued unemployment is essentially their own concern and the community's. It will be recalled that a combination of private and governmental programs was envisioned by the President's Advisory Committee on Labor-Management Policy as the most feasible way of treating technological displacement.

The record in coal epitomizes the breath-taking promise of "automation." It also reveals the concomitant disruption of workers' lives and the serious social problems that are involved.

One of the great strengths of collective bargaining is in its capacity for devising practical solutions to meet particular problems of the private sector of the economy. Like the coal and the meat-packing arrangements, the much discussed West Coast Longshore Agreement could not have been created nor its mutual benefits realized except by agreement among the parties themselves.

After extended debate in 1958, representatives of the longshoremen "voted unanimously to explore with the employers the benefits to be gained if they were to adopt a cooperative policy for orderly introduction of new mechanical methods and changes in working rules."[2] The

²William Glazier, "Automation and the Longshoremen," *Atlantic Monthly*, December 1960.

Pacific Maritime Association decided that through cooperation with the Union, a free hand to mechanize could be realized effectively. In the collective agreement dated October 26, 1960, the union conceded management's right freely to mechanize and without regard to previously established work rules, including those regulating crew sizes. In return the companies agreed to contribute a sizable amount to an "automation fund" to protect the interests of affected employees. This reconciliation of diverse interests was brought about by an agreement, ratified by a majority of the workers, which met the circumstances of a particular case. As in the coal industry, workers have been displaced and there will be a marked shrinkage of job opportunities in longshoring. Costs to society are a part of technological advance if the interests of affected employees are to be taken into account.

The examples of collective bargaining agreements which accelerate and facilitate technological change would be incomplete without some reference to those under which the introduction of new machines and methods is synchronized with employee attrition rates in order to avoid displacement altogether. To the extent that attrition rates lag, cost savings will have to be deferred. In an increasing number of cases, however, companies are guaranteeing that "no regular employee shall lose his job in consequence of technological changes." This policy can be difficult to administer. A clear differentiation between job losses due to the specified cause and those occasioned by seasonal or cyclical variations of demand is often not possible. And, overtime work, even at premium rates of pay, will sometimes be scheduled as the alternative to engaging new employees. Nevertheless, particular circumstances sometimes make this approach feasible.

In point is the policy of the Transit Authority of the City of New York. As one part of the settlement of the labor agreement dispute with the Transport Workers of America in December, 1961, the Authority agreed to make explicit its established policy in this area. A letter, supplementary to the labor agreement, reads:

> The Transit Authority in carrying out its managerial responsibilities for the safe and efficient operation of the transit facilities under its jurisdiction has introduced many efficiencies by automation and other means. In effecting these operating improvements, the Authority has consistently adhered to the policy of not laying off any permanent employees by assigning surplus employees to other productive work without any reduction in the employee's pay. . . .

That policy, more than any other single influence, seems to have made it possible for the Authority to introduce technological changes over the years. Its operations were conducted in 1961 with approximately 27,500 employees; a reduction of about 6,500 employees as compared to 1955.

There is, then, ample evidence of the widespread acceptance by unions of the high wage-low labor cost doctrine under which improved methods of production are encouraged as long as employee needs are also satisfied. In order to do this, a combination of private and government programs is the key.

It is now suggested that, in many ways, the collective bargaining approach has advantages over the making of technological changes by a company without the formal checks and balances of collective bargaining. One cannot assume that non-unionized operations, in themselves, provide a smooth road for management. Unorganized workers are as much concerned as everyone else in job security and a fair share of productivity gains.

As early as 1931, a publication appeared (by Stanley B. Mathewson) concerning the restriction of output by unorganized workers. Being unorganized, the employees studied were particularly vulnerable to the disciplinary action, heavily counted upon in earlier years, to induce a "fair day's work." Yet, restriction of production was found to be deeply entrenched and well-nigh universally practiced among virtually all employee groups. It was a response to the challenge of job insecurity and a reaction "on principle" to what were appraised as unfair terms of employment.

Restriction of production, as a form of employee self-protection, existed long before the 1931 Inquiry and has since continued as an active force. In 1949, Peter Drucker wrote about this matter (in *The New Society*) as follows:

> . . . open restrictions on efficiency and productivity are only the part of the iceberg that is above water. Much more important are the invisible, unwritten, informal restrictions decreed by the custom and the common law of every plant . . . bosses have learned, however, that an attempt to break the production code of their department will bring nothing but serious trouble. They also sympathize as a rule with the men's attitude—they themselves may well share the workers' fear that increased productivity may cost them their job.

Neither employees nor foremen have an inherent conviction that they can freely contribute to production increases "without [according to Mathewson] incurring penalties in place of the rewards which usually accompany special attention to duty in other fields of endeavor." Yet, "most working people hate the whole messy business of restriction, and especially the complicated system of cunning devices they employ to cover it up."

The direct representation of employees by a union at least permits a facing up to and a direct dealing with those forces upon which the employee contribution to production is so dependent. Due process can supplant the often capricious unwritten laws and mores of the workplace. Many a management, unable to develop a satisfactory personnel policy, has attested in private conversation that dealing with a responsible union has improved the productive performance of employees. This is, of course, not a pre-ordained result, but neither does the absence of a union inevitably solve the problem.

On two counts, then, collective bargaining is a national asset in adjusting to the technological change which is under way. It provides an effective procedure for a practical reconciliation of conflicting objectives of management and the employees. To the extent that acquiescence of employees to the necessary adjustments is secured, a major contribution can be made to the effective utilization of new equipment and new methods.

WHAT ABOUT FEATHERBEDDING?

The wide degree of acceptance of technological change by unions can, thus, be demonstrated. Nevertheless, there is a gnawing general belief that the cost-saving benefits of such changes are, as a rule, dissipated by union adherence to capricious work rules which perpetuate unnecessary jobs and create unneeded hours of work. Extensive substantive evidence is at hand to provide a basis for the belief. Stand-by musicians and pilot truck drivers do secure choice job protection for themselves but at costs that can adversely affect prices and consumer demand. It should be possible to meet their demands for job security in more constructive ways. In one situation, the usefulness of a new machine was in grave doubt because of the employees' insistence upon production quotas, long established on older machines, which actually resulted in but six hours of actual work in an eight-hour day. The examples could be, but need not be, multiplied.

Such a high priority is presently being given to increased productivity, however, as to make popular the petulant dismissal of every inhibiting work rule as a simple case of "featherbedding" that should be eliminated forthwith. This has caused strikes. The trouble with the cavalier treatment is that "featherbedding" is not such a simple subject and can only be appraised on a case-by-case basis.

Some work rules unreasonably give preferential treatment to those who, in shop vernacular, "ride the gravy train." These rules are commonly though silently resented by fellow workers. If they are specifically identified, their prompt elimination is usually feasible. On the other hand, many work rules, formal and informal, stem from an understandable desire of individuals to reduce their exposure to the economic risk inherent in a system of employment and of pay by the hour. In a part of the sugar refining industry it took the introduction of a kind of guaranteed annual wage to make a number of rigid work rules unprized by the employees. Under collective bargaining, the costs of work rules are formalized and on the table. For reasons already enunciated, it is a moot question whether collectively bargained work rules actually involve greater costs than the informal rules to which unorganized, as well as organized, workers adhere. This much is clear—work rules cannot be dealt with either as isolated phenomena or as "one ball of wax." A part of economic wisdom is to appreciate the depths that are plumbed in digging into work rules.

Some work rules are quite incomprehensible unless they are evaluated in terms of the individual's desire for personal status, so elusive in a workaday life embodying but little opportunity for personal triumphs. Rules in this area have odd manifestations. In one instance, the senior employees of a plant somehow gained a highly prized preference; their fellows allowed them to go first in punching out the time clock. The exit of the venerables from the parking lot was eased and they liked that. This particular informal rule, as it happened, also contributed to efficiency. Eliminated was another informal practice of everybody quitting work quite early in order to engage in what had been a sort of Oklahoma land rush to the time clocks.

Other work rules seem to represent a conscious choice of leisure over the greater productivity which could presumably make higher wages possible. The extended coffee break, provision for wash-up time and the like are examples. There are no more highly valued work rules in industrial relations and union leaders recommend a relinquishment at their peril. Along with provisions for longer vacations and more paid holidays such work rules can even be considered as one aspect of the longtime trend to shorter hours of work without a reduction in the weekly wage. Leisure is a normal personal goal.

The so-called featherbedding issue thus involves thousands of highly-particularized problems not amenable to understanding or treatment through broad generalization. A failure to recognize this fact can have disastrous consequences. No more sobering example can be referred to than the intensification of the 1959 steel strike by management's raising of the "2-B" issue in a way that was interpreted as a drive for unilateral management right to change work rules.

Work rules applicable to the utilization of labor cannot be summarily dismissed en masse as long as the conservation of those human values which individuals prize remains among the important goals. It is a sign of the times, perhaps, that the short-shrift treatment is so largely confined to those rules which benefit hourly paid workers while work rules prevalent in the professions, including college teaching with its tenure appointments, are more sympathetically viewed. Arrangements for balancing producers' interests with consumers' interests reflect a common desire to make one's working life more secure and more comfortable. Work rules are obviously neither an invention nor a monopoly of organized hourly workers. A defense of some forms of "featherbedding" is not difficult to mount.

WAGE RATES AND TECHNOLOGICAL CHANGE

In "The Annual Report of the Council of Economic Advisers" submitted to the President on January 12, 1962, the specified general guide for noninflationary wage behavior "is that the rate of increase in wage rates (including fringe benefits) in each industry be equal to the trend rate of over-all productivity increase." Special modifications of the general guides, to "reconcile them with objectives of equity and efficiency" are recognized to be necessary in particular industries. It is proposed that

(1) Wage rate increases would exceed the general guide rate in an industry which would otherwise be unable to attract sufficient labor; or in which wage rates are exceptionally low compared with the range of wages earned elsewhere by similar labor, because the bargaining position of workers has been weak in particular local labor markets. (2) Wage rate increases would fall short of the general guide rate in an industry which could not provide jobs for its entire labor force even in times of generally full employment; or in which wage rates are exceptionally high compared with the range of wages earned elsewhere by similar labor, because the bargaining position of workers has been especially strong.

Enunciation of that wage policy by the Council fundamentally is an expression of the great public interest in the qualitative terms of labor agreements. It also represents a conclusion that "collective bargaining as usual" cannot safely be relied upon to allocate the benefits of technology. The disquiet about collective bargaining obviously derives from an intensification of national needs for high productivity, full utilization of resources, low costs and a stable currency in an extremely critical period of our history. How can these broader requirements adequately be dealt with through an institution designed essentially to reconcile the conflicting private interests affected by so-called automation? And, how can the results of collective bargaining be compatible with national objectives when the relative economic power in particular situations fashions the terms of agreement? Similar questions have been raised, it should be noted, not only as respects private wage determination but private price determination as well. There can be no doubt that another dimension is being added to collective bargaining—restraint in the public interest as respects both resort to work stoppages and the fixing of agreement terms.

When the world environment was less exacting of us and when national planning was more limited in scope and less imperative, the public interest in collective bargaining was confined mainly to having uninterrupted production, i.e., a minimum resort to strikes. This particular interest has been greatly intensified, especially in respect to such operations as missile bases. And in 1962 a repeat of the 1959 steel strike was deemed unacceptable by the public. President Kennedy expressed the public interest in steel negotiations by insisting not only upon an "early settlement" but upon substantive terms of settlement which would not necessitate price increases. The reality of the demand for purposeful attention to national interests in private decision making was forcibly demonstrated in the 1962 steel negotiations, which doubtless will go into the records as a major event in the country's economic history.

The public is now deeply concerned with the quality of the terms of settlement. Such an interest had previously existed in any degree of intensity only during World War II and the Korean engagement. The policies brought into being in those periods, however, are no pattern for the present. Wage and price controls are not acceptable but neither is "collective bargaining as usual." The direction indicated is for collective bargaining not as usual. This raises the question of institutional changes in the process.

INSTITUTIONAL CHANGES

Changes in the forms and practices of collective bargaining, to provide a requisite regard for the public interests, constitute the new frontier in labor-management relations. More than mere routine procedural modifications form the substance of these developments. The manifold problems of technological change can only be resolved through analytical processes and not by "crisis bargaining" culminating in the arbitrament by relative economic power. New problem-solving mechanisms have to be invented. This observation made recently by Barbara Ward is pertinent:

> The fundamental question is whether we in the West are able to confront the challenge of our times. And here we face the agonizing difficulty that some of the creative responses we need to make run deeply against the grain of our traditional thinking.

One of the creative responses to effect institutional changes in collective bargaining, involving public understanding as well as union statesmanship, would come about by a reappraisal of "appropriate units of representation" of employees. Various experiments in the participation of "informed neutrals" in collective bargaining at the invitation of the parties are already under way and are of interest. The substitution of continuous negotiation for crisis bargaining is also an important area for developing improved practices. Along all these lines, the "creative response" to the need for institutional change is being expressed. A brief discussion of each of them follows.

Appropriate unit of representation

Treatment of this subject calls for a considered balancing of the dangers of the great concentration of power in industry-wide unions with the instability of small unions with but limited jurisdiction and responsible only to protect narrow employee interests. Industry-wide strikes can impinge upon the public right to be free from total interruption of vital services; so-called whip-sawing and the narrow representation of small employee interest groups can interfere with the public right to orderly bargaining and reasonably restrained wage movements.

Some unions may be too strong; others may be too weak to fulfill their responsibilities. It is often said, for example, that there is nowhere a private power concentration comparable to that possessed by the United Steelworkers in its capacity to shut down entirely one of the most basic of all industries. To be sure, selective strikes by industry-wide unions would avoid a complete stoppage of output. It is moot, however, as to whether that would limit union bargaining power. An enhancement of bargaining power would more likely result. On the other hand, narrow representational units serving fragmented interest groups can also create problems that seem overwhelming. Recent public emergency disputes in the maritime industry and in the airline industry are illustrative. The mechanisms and procedures used by most industry-wide unions to mediate between the conflicting objectives of employees are quite lacking in maritime. Separate bargaining between a large number of unions and the employers is, in consequence, carried out under extreme handicaps and has often been less than orderly or restrained. How does a problem get solved when each of a number of unions insists that the employers adopt its own particular solution or "take a strike"? In the airline industry, several Presidential Emergency Boards have concluded that a merger of the pilots and the flight engineers' unions would assist materially in achieving a fair and constructive resolution of the critical manning issues on jet aircraft. Crises occur because of a lack of industry-wide bargaining as frequently as they do because of this setup.

There are strong reasons, then, for identifying "appropriate unit of representation" as major aspect of institutional change requirement in the collective bargaining area. Numerous experiments to effect the desired changes are under way. Some national unions have sought to synchronize their bargaining programs. The International Association of Machinists and the United Automobile Workers, for example, have frequently done so in the airframe industry. Establishment of the tripartite *ad hoc* board in the railroad industry, in 1959, to consider the persistent work rules issue had, among its innovations, the virtue of bringing to one forum the several employee organizations whose interests overlap. A novel organizational structure for collective bargaining was created, by Presidential Executive Order dated May 26, 1961, more adequately to deal with labor disputes at missile and space sites and to insure more economical operations there. The order was issued following wide consultation with the representatives of construction concerns, manufacturers and labor unions involved and was accompanied by a no-strike commitment by the unions. A basic feature of the order, as noted in a letter dated May 25, 1961 from Secretary of Labor Goldberg to President George Meany, was establishing

> . . . at each missile or space site, a Missile Site Labor Relations Committee, composed of manufacturing and construction concerns, labor organizations, contracting agencies and mediators assigned by the Federal Mediation and Conciliation Service. These committees would forecast impending problems, arranging for their settlement before they became acute, using fully all existing voluntary procedures and devising new adequate procedures where none exist.

A ready solution of all missile site problems is not assured and is not likely, but the setting up of collective bargaining procedures better adapted to the circumstances of missile site operation is an outstanding instance of creative thinking in the field of institutional change.

There are ironic, offsetting debits. The risks of technological change, notably the fear of job insecurity, have sparked attempts to perpetuate, and even to extend, units of representation protective of narrow group interests. The intensified conflict within the AFL-CIO over the exclusive job jurisdictions of the constituent bodies is in point. Significant, too, is a growing craft consciousness of employees in many manufacturing and service industries. Their drive for smaller bargaining units is emphatically not grounded upon an employee belief that work rules should be less restrictive or wage increases more moderate.

In a case involving the New York Transit Authority several years ago, 17 occupational groups of employees sought to break away from the system-wide Transport Workers Union and to establish their own separate bargaining units. The dispute was fortunately resolved by a change in internal union structures to assure more effective craft and occupational participation within the larger unit of representation. A retention of that larger unit, with its greater power concentration, was a *sine qua non* for the public right to uninterrupted service and to permit an accommodation of diverse interests within the union as a prerequisite for orderly bargaining with the Transit Authority.

The unit of representation question also brings up the question of proper relationship between a national union and affiliated local unions. A local union willing to agree to terms deemed favorable by an employer has been occasionally forestalled by the "national union office." It is then typically suggested that local bargaining should be encouraged as a matter of principle. Yet, the record shows that local union autonomy also carries a high potentiality for precipitating strikes and extreme demands. In my experience in this area, the major function of most national union officials has been to induce local unions to exercise restraint. Not infrequently, such counsel is provided upon request of the employer.

The answer to union power seems clear at least when expressed as a general principle. A union should have the power and the representational jurisdiction required for the performance of the functions it is expected to perform. They include the protection of employee interests which requires mediating between the conflicting and extreme demands of the various employee groups that comprise the membership. This is an essential step in the consummation of a labor agreement protective not only of employee interests but of employer and public interests as well. Performance of such exacting functions, especially selling employees on the need for restraint in the public interest, implies the possession of a considerable power. Whether or not unions have earned the confidence and respect of the public to a degree that would induce the granting of the requisite power is quite another story beyond the scope of this discussion. However, it is the enhanced public interest in the avoidance of strikes plus a new interest in the qualitative terms of settlement that necessitates evaluation of the union power question from a new point of view. The optimum size for the efficient performance of union functions is a possible criterion.

Tripartite collective bargaining

The great interest aroused by the several instances in which "informed neutrals" have been invited to participate in labor-management negotiations, as well as the attacks made upon this kind of institutional change, seem to constitute a lot of attention to what is as yet no more than a promising experiment. Perhaps these responses reflect how intense the hope is in some quarters for an improved collective bargaining and how deep the resistance to change runs in others.

There is no necessity here to spell out the details of third-party participation under the labor agreements at Armour and Company, the Kaiser Steel Company, and the New York Transit Authority among others. Or, to discuss the tripartite setup to deal with the work-rules and compensation issues on the railroads. Material on the provisions of the plans is profuse. Suffice it now to underline that in each case the "outsiders" sit in only upon the invitation of both the union and the management and have only such functions as are specified jointly by these parties. There is no compulsion about this matter.

It is not easy to delineate clearly and precisely the functions of third-party participants. They do include, however, a kind of private mediation. This means the mediating is undertaken by persons known to the parties and chosen by them. They are presumably relatively familiar with the background and the nuances of problems on the table. That could have some advantage as compared to *ad hoc* mediation, provided under the law, by persons less familiar with the case. Beyond that, a new staff function is introduced. In these days of change, the line managements of companies, and unions as well, have deemed it practical if not essential to rely upon their own staff officers for assistance in their own unilateral decision-making. There is no doubt that these staff officers are playing an increasingly important role in the formulation of the position of each side. However, collective bargaining is joint decision-making and it is characterized by increasing complexity of issues and greater importance to everybody. It could well be that a major benefit of third-party participation would be in their serving as staff advisors to the joint decision-makers in an extension of the long established line-staff principles which are standard in modern business organizations. In this capacity, the "outsiders" could conceivably suggest a phrasing of the problems mutually faced in such a way so as to facilitate their resolution and they might be in a better position to express the public interest.

The responsibility of third-party participants for making recommendations under certain conditions doubtless accounts for most of the antipathy shown by companies and unions alike toward the experiments underway. For here is an outside intrusion, even if invited, that casts doubt upon the long-standing principle that wage determination and the related negotiations are exclusively a private matter. Recommendations can effect relative bargaining positions. The dilemma is similar, in some ways, to that faced by the framers of the emergency dispute section of the Taft-Hartley Act. Under that Act, even after a Presidential finding of national emergency, a Board of Inquiry lacks the authority to make recommendations. The handwriting on the wall, however, seems to say that in public emergency disputes, there are instances when the public interest will assert itself clearly and poignantly as respects what has hitherto been looked upon as exclusively private negotiations.

Sooner or later, Boards of Inquiry will be authorized to make recommendations as to the basis of settlement. This is not the same, however, as providing more generally for recommendations. The public interest in effective negotiations is in a sense voluntarily conceded by those parties who have invited third-party participation in their regular negotiations. This "runs deeply against the grain of our traditional thinking." For whatever reason, many persons would not class third-party participation as a "creative response" at all.

A few words about the real nature of mediatory recommendations are in order to dispel the contention that they are, in fact, a form of compulsory arbitration. This is simply not the case. An arbitrator with the power to decide weighs the evidence and then, on the basis of the terms of submission, expresses his own conviction of what constitutes a fair and equitable settlement. In a sense, the terms are imposed though in voluntary arbitration through a procedure agreed to by the parties, themselves. In marked contrast, in fashioning his recommendations a mediator seeks to discover those terms that will either be mutually acceptable to the parties or that will provide a starting point from which they can work out terms to which they can agree. Unlike arbitration, either party is free to reject recommendations out-of-hand. A mediator fails if his recommendations do not provide a basis for agreement. In short, the parameters of the mediator's problem are entirely different from the arbitrator's. It is desirable and proper that the usefulness of "outside" recommendations be vigorously debated especially during these early stages of experiment with third-party participation. It is not constructive, however, to evaluate this institutional change by advancing arguments, which are formidable, against compulsory arbitration.

One of the consequences of the increasing public stake in uninterrupted production, and especially in the qualitative terms of labor agreements, is that collective bargaining is no longer such a private matter as it once was. There is a distinct possibility that the current experiments in third-party participation will prove to be increasingly acceptable to unions and to managements as the need for analytical methods for dealing with their problems becomes more pressing.

Continuous negotiation

Amid the steel negotiations for a new labor contract in February 1962, it was authoritatively reported that the previously established Human Relations Research Committee, composed of company and union representatives, had laid important groundwork for a renewal. They did so by making joint recommendations in such areas as "simplifying and speeding up the grievance procedure," and for creation of a joint task force to study job classifications and review classification methods. As respects seniority, agreement was reached, it was reported, as to how the issue should be phrased, i.e., in terms of the creation of broader-based labor pools with some provision for preferential hiring between plants of the same company on the basis of seniority and possibly providing some consideration beyond severance pay for permanently displaced employees. A clear statement of an issue can often represent half of its resolution.

The importance of these events is in removing certain problems from the "crisis collective bargaining" arena where they can only be dealt with under inhibiting limitations imposed by an imminent strike deadline. There is ample experience to prove that issues such as seniority are unlikely to be intelligently handled on the eve of a contract expiration. The right to strike must be retained, of course, as the final arbitrament of labor disputes in a free society. However, as a means of exerting pressure to resolve problems, with the increasing scope of collective bargaining, the strike should be viewed as a special-purpose tool and not a general-purpose tool. It will help to settle some issues but not others. Some issues can only be adequately dealt with on the basis of careful investigation and evaluation of the facts and in the absence of economic pressure. The Human Relations Research Committee in steel has pioneered new territory in dealing with many problems apart from the crisis bargaining arena. A promising way toward constructive institutional change has been mapped out.

CONCLUSION

The conclusion is brief. Collective bargaining is an institution which has effectively provided for a reconciliation of employee and management interests in making adjustments to technological change. It is a relatively new institution but has shown a capacity to adjust to changing environments. At a time of great world tensions and enormous national need, the environment has become more exacting of collective bargaining than ever before. Of greatest significance, the public interests which are affected by private collective bargaining have become wider in scope and more critical in nature. Institutional changes effected by the parties themselves in order to adjust to this circumstance are of paramount importance. In the larger sense, this is true of many of our democratic institutions and the stakes are great. In the words of Robert M. Hutchins, ". . . if our hopes of democracy are to be realized, the next generation is in for a job of institutional remodeling the like of which has not been seen since the Founding Fathers." One need not go that far while still visualizing institutional adjustments as the most promising way of creating a collective bargaining in tune with the demands of the second half of the twentieth century.

W. Allen Wallis

6

Some Economic Considerations

THE SOURCE OF INNOVATION

A common view is that technological innovation, like the Mississippi, just goes rolling along, year in and year out, at a steady, sure pace, on an inevitable and predictable course.

This view has derived its most effective support from the late William F. Ogburn and his associate, S. C. Gilfillan, particularly from the former's *Social Change* (1933) and the latter's *Sociology of Invention* (1935). As the stream of culture flows on, generation after generation, it accumulates bits and pieces of knowledge and technique. These bits and pieces fit together into inventions or innovations. When the essential bits and pieces have come into existence through cultural evolution, it is inevitable that someone—in fact, often several people independently —will fit them together to form the innovation.

This innovation itself then moves along in the current of culture, becoming in its turn one of the bits and pieces destined in due course to be fitted into some other innovation. In this inexorable process, some inventions occur long before there is any social need for them; others fail to occur despite long and acute need, according to whether the times are right or wrong for them. Gilfillan has tried his hand, with

W. ALLEN WALLIS *is Dean of the Graduate School of Business at the University of Chicago and Professor of Statistics and Economics. During World War II Mr. Wallis was director of the Statistical Research Group of the Office of Scientific Research and Development; and in 1959-61 was a Special Assistant to President Eisenhower. A board member of several organizations, both public and private, he is author of many books and articles on statistics and economics.*

some success, at predicting inventions in advance. One of his earliest attempts is one of the most fascinating, his article entitled "The Future Home Theater," *The Independent,* October 17, 1912. This predicted television. There is little similarity technically between modern television and his forecasts, and his timing was very much premature, but he made some penetrating forecasts of the social consequences of television—as well as some that are wide of the mark.

In sharp contrast to the view that innovations result from the stream of culture just rolling along are the views that they result from transcendent revelations, striking great geniuses like lightning, or that they result from the industry, perseverance, and intelligence of dedicated, self-reliant individuals. These views are as rare today as the view that people who are unsuccessful or anti-social are responsible for their own shortcomings, not society.

A third view is that innovation results from social organization for adapting what is possible to what is desirable. Our own social organization provides for seeking innovations in diverse ways simultaneously: through the lone-wolf "ingenious Yankee," through the scientific genius, through a corps of engineers and technicians, through large scientific laboratories, through tightly organized, closely programmed industrial organizations for research and development, through the vast informal network that has been dubbed by Michael Polanyi "the republic of science." Social organization is involved in making accessible to these diverse participants the accumulating knowledge and technology of society, in indicating to them social needs and priorities, in providing them support, and in giving them incentives to get the greatest yield in relation to resources spent. The process has been described by Richard Nelson[1] as "the interplay of moving frontiers of knowledge and growing need upon the direction and likelihood of success of individual 'acts of novelty.' "

This third view of innovation is, of course, a special case of the economist's general view of social economic organization.[2] This view, in broad terms, is that the efforts of people as consumers to obtain as much satisfaction as possible from their limited incomes, and the efforts of the same people as producers to get as much income as possible from their limited resources and capacities to work, interact to set prices of consumers' goods and of productive services in such a way that the relation between the prices of any two things measures their relative scarcity or abundance in terms of their ability to satisfy wants. High prices tend to stimulate production of the high-priced things, as a means of increasing the incomes of productive services; at the same time, high prices tend to reduce the consumption of the high-priced things, as a means of con-

[1] "The Economics of Incentive," *Journal of Business,* 1959.
[2] See F. A. Hayek, "The Use of Knowledge in Society," *American Economic Review,* 1945, and Frank H. Knight, *Economic Organization.*

serving the incomes of consumers for other uses. The social organization brought about through these price or market mechanisms governs what shall be produced, by whom, with what resources, and by what methods; and governs consumption similarly. It may be viewed as an elaborate mechanism for combining information on general, over-all priorities, with information on the specific circumstances of time and place; and at the same time as a mechanism for providing a powerful incentive to conform to the implications of the messages about what should be conserved and what may be used freely.

In such a view of the social economic organization, innovation is induced by complex relations among prices and costs, and more specifically by opportunities to change those relations in such a way that the change will redound to the benefit of the person making the change. This view does not imply that inventions can be ordered custom-fitted and delivered on schedule, nor that inventors are motivated exclusively by pecuniary gain. It does imply that technological developments are not autonomous, outside the influence of economic forces, but are influenced by economic forces just as they influence economic forces.

The development of textile machinery in the late eighteenth century can be interpreted, in this view, as the result of a major effort by the social organization. The earlier improvements in commerce and agriculture had made food and fibers more abundant, and had created the possibility of transferring some people from agricultural production to other activities. Improved engineering technology made it possible to develop machines for handling cotton and wool. The combination of these circumstances presented eighteenth century society with a challenge and an opportunity, out of which sprang the industrial revolution.

A similar interpretation can be placed on the development of transportation in the early nineteenth century. Continued expansion of population and industry faced a serious constraint if transportation remained tied to waterways. If the vast land areas and resources of the United States were to attain economic value there had to be means of transportation over land. Faced with this barrier to its continued expansion, the social economic organization made a sustained and successful assault on the transportation problem.

The development and introduction of automation should be viewed in similar terms. To some extent the elements that make automation possible have come about through cultural evolution: through achievements of science pursued for science's sake, through military developments, and through by-products of research and development on such problems as communication. Vigorous efforts to apply these elements to automation result from an acute social need to get as much output as possible in relation to the number of people employed. The precise magnitude and nature of such social needs, and of opportunities for meeting them, is communicated through prices—more precisely, through the relations of prices to one another. Prices also constitute a strong incentive to utilize the opportunities to meet the needs summarized by the messages, for this is the way to higher incomes.

DEVELOPMENT AND INTRODUCTION OF TECHNOLOGICAL CHANGE

In considering economic factors in technological innovation, including automation, a distinction should be made between the development of technology and its adoption. The factors influencing development differ in part from those influencing introduction.

There is a difference between the organizational arrangements by which our economy develops new techniques of production, and in particular techniques of automation, and the arrangements by which it develops new products. New products are developed mostly in laboratories serving a single firm whose main business is the production of such products, not research and development. New methods of production, however, are developed mostly in laboratories that serve all of industry. Since the outcome of research is uncertain, there is a substantial risk in new product development that any basic research will produce results whose value, if any, relates to products not made by the company. Consequently, research on new products tends to be confined to large companies with diverse product lines. (Results of research can, of course, be sold or licensed to other firms. This mitigates, but only partially, the drawbacks to a firm of supporting a laboratory whose results may not contribute to the firm's own product lines. Also, there are a few firms which specialize in developing new products for other firms to produce, but these are not a significant factor in developing new products.)

But for a firm engaged in producing automation equipment there is much greater assurance that any new discoveries it makes will fit its own business, since it does not expect to use the results itself but to sell them wherever they may have value in the production of a service or commodity. This difference in organization suggests the conjecture that automation may be the object of somewhat more intensive research and development than it otherwise would, in comparison with new products, simply because new discoveries in automation are more likely to redound to the direct benefit of the discovering firm.

Another factor working in the direction of disproportionate efforts to develop automation is the great need for automation in modern weapons systems. Many of the control devices developed for aircraft, ships, missiles, and space vehicles can be applied to, or modified for, the control of production processes. Perhaps more important, the basic science and technology that is created in developing weapons systems, and even more the scientists and technologists themselves, can be utilized in developing automation.

Technological progress is, presumably, directly related to the amount of industrial research. The amount invested in industrial research is directly related to the profits produced by research. From 1950 to 1960, annual expenditures on industrial research, adjusted for price changes, grew by 12 percent per year, a rate which implies doubling annual expenditures every six years. A principal reason for this extraordinarily rapid growth was that funds invested in research yielded a higher return than funds invested in other ways. The differential return on research over other investments appears to have diminished, and it has been estimated by Yale Brozen[3] that expenditures on research in the 1960's will show only half the percentage rate of growth of the 1950's. Perhaps, then, the 60's will see a decline in this component of the forces tending toward disproportionate efforts to invent new automation methods.

The simple fact that capital is being accumulated faster than the labor force is growing tends to stimulate automation. The increasing amount of capital per worker means that the additional capital must, so to speak, be self-operating; that is, workers cannot be assigned to capital in the same ratio as formerly, and if the capital is to operate fully, each worker must be able to tend more of it. The process by which our social-economic organization brings about this adjustment to the increasing ratio of capital to labor may be described, in the schematizations of economic analysis, as follows: As the amount of capital outstrips the labor force, a rise in wages comes about because owners of the additional capital, trying to find labor to operate it, attempt to "pirate" employees from other firms. The higher wages make it more profitable than formerly to develop labor-saving devices; or, to put it differently, some labor-saving devices which formerly would not have saved enough in wages to offset their own costs, hence were not developed, now save more than enough in wages to offset their costs, so are developed.

The analysis of the preceding paragraph applies to efforts to develop new automation techniques. Successful development of such techniques will bring greater rewards to the developer, now that the quantity of capital has increased relative to the quantity of labor, so more intensive efforts will be made (i.e., more costs will be incurred) in the effort to develop new techniques. But the analysis applies to the adoption of existing techniques, as well as to the development of new ones.

There are in existence at any time many labor-saving devices that are technically feasible but economically wasteful. Machinery for handling materials, for example, was introduced a decade or two earlier in the

[3] "The Future of Industrial Research," *Journal of Business,* 1961.

United States than in Great Britain. Materials handling techniques were, of course, known in Britain as soon as in the United States, if for no other reason than that technological communication between the two countries is virtually as free, fast, and fluid as within them. Britain's "lag" can be accounted for in large part by its lower ratio of labor costs to capital costs, and according to Seymour Melman, in *Dynamic Factors in Industrial Productivity,* when the introduction of machinery for handling materials came in Britain it was because the ratio of labor costs to capital costs had risen. Similarly, automation of an automobile assembly line was technically successful in the Morris plant in England in 1927, but was economically unsuccessful because the cost of the labor saved was less than the cost of saving it.

WAGES

One step in the process described above, by which an increase in the quantity of capital stimulates automation, is an increase in wages. The increase in wages leads in turn to the development and introduction of labor-saving devices. An increase in wages will have this effect, whether it results from a larger amount of capital or from some other cause.

A particular industry which has experienced no increase, or even a decrease, in capital may find itself faced with a rise in wages because other industries are increasing in size and are successfully bidding labor away from it. This rise in wages will trigger the effort to introduce labor-saving techniques. Thus, even a declining industry may be forced to develop and introduce automation in order to raise its output per man-hour, and thus be able to meet higher wage rates prevailing in the rest of the economy.

There may be important differences, however, in how far the process of saving labor is carried, depending on the forces creating the rise in wages. In the case described above, where the rise in wages results from bidding among owners of capital whose capital would go untended (more precisely, under-tended), the process of automating to get along with less labor per unit of capital is self-limiting. As automation makes it possible for each worker to utilize more capital, the need to "pirate" labor declines, so the tendency for wages to rise disappears after they have gone up a certain amount. Thus, the displacement of labor by automation halts before it goes so far as to cause unemployment. (More accurately, this is what *would* happen if the ratio of capital to labor stabilized at a new, higher level. Actually, of course, the ratio is continuing to rise, so the upward pressure on wages is maintained. The introduction of labor-saving devices therefore continues. Nevertheless, it does not reach a rate leading to unemployment, for if it did the upward pressure on wages would halt and thereby halt the process of displacing labor.)

Where the rise in wages comes about through other forces it may induce an uneconomic degree of automation, that is, one that is wasteful because it goes so far as to displace labor for which there are not other employment opportunities as productive as those from which it is displaced. This effect will be most pronounced in industries where there are good technical possibilities of replacing labor by machines, as is often the case in industries which have long production runs on nearly identical items, for example, cigarettes or automobiles. It has been estimated, by Stephen Sobotka (*Profile of Michigan*) that in the automobile industry a given small percentage rise in wages will lead to the introduction of enough labor-saving machinery to cause about three times as large a percentage decrease in employment. If, then, unions in the industry can raise wages five percent above what they otherwise would be, employment in the industry will be 15 percent below what it otherwise would be.

This 15 percent is not necessarily unemployed, to be sure; instead they are employed in other industries, where, by swelling the labor supply they have the effect of lowering wages, and where productivity tends to be lower because capital has been drawn away for the automobile industry. Thus, automation in the automobile industry may be carried to a point where it is uneconomic and wasteful in the twofold sense that too much capital is drawn into automobile production out of other uses, and that too much labor is forced out of automobile production into other uses. The fault, of course, lies not in automation itself, but in the forces which cause uneconomic automation in some industries by holding wage levels out of line with other industries.

Uneconomic automation can be induced also by forces that tend to lower artificially the cost of new equipment in comparison with the cost of old equipment. A special tax privilege for new equipment, for example, would lead to somewhat earlier scrapping of old equipment and replacement by new than accords with the amounts of resources consumed by the two pieces of equipment to get a given amount of output. In general, the availability of new machines requiring a smaller input of labor, power, and materials than is required to produce the same output on old machines does not necessarily mean that it is economically efficient to scrap the old machines. For the old machine to be scrapped, the saving of inputs by the new machine should be sufficient to compensate for the excess of the capital cost of the new machine over the salvage value of the old one. If the cost of the new machine is reduced by special tax privileges not accorded old machines, this necessary margin of advantage in the cost of inputs is less, and some automation will be profitable, and will be introduced, that would not have been introduced without the tax privilege. In short, the tax privilege can serve as an inducement to uneconomic displacement of labor, that is, displacement of labor before more productive alternative employment is available.

GENERAL LEVEL OF EMPLOYMENT

In considering the effects of automation on the general level of employment, it is important to recognize that building automation equipment, though it may reduce the total number of man-hours of work required over a long period, has the effect of redistributing the employment in time. Work that without automation would have been done in the future is, in effect, done now in building the machine. Suppose a pinsetting machine is being built for a bowling alley. When the machine is installed it will eliminate many man-hours of pinsetting labor. But during the period of its construction employment is actually increased, for more man-hours per day will be used during its construction than are being used to set pins. In fact, manual setting of pins will continue while the machine is being built, so the work on building the machine is clear addition to the total volume of employment. Thus, in a sense, automation replaces a long trickle of employment by an initial splash.

This does not mean, either, that because of the initial splash of employment on building automation equipment a subsequent drought is in store. It sometimes happens—bowling may be a case in point—that automation leads, through price reductions or quality improvements, to so large an expansion in the industry that total employment is larger after automation is complete than it would be, even allowing for secular growth, without automation. This is not, however, typical.

A more general reason why doing the work of the future now does not mean future unemployment is that the total amount of work to be done in the future is infinite. Yale Brozen[4] has estimated that it would require $2 trillion ($2 \times 10^{12}$) of net investment to automate all of American industry. If the net supply of savings is $20 billion ($2 \times 10^{10}$) per year above what is needed to provide capital equipment for the growth of the labor force—and the figure is not likely to be higher in the near future—this would imply a century to get the job done. (It would not actually take that long, for the savings available would average more than $20 billion in a period as long as a century; but, on the other hand, new products and new technology will almost certainly push the required investment for total automation continually higher.)

In short, the problem of general unemployment from automation is a non-existent will-o'-the-wisp problem.

[4] *Automation and Society,* ed. Jackson and Roucek.

DISLOCATIONS

To the extent that there are real problems of unemployment associated with automation, they are problems of dislocation. Current construction, installation, and maintenance of pinsetting machines is creating more employment than if all existing bowling alleys were using pin boys; but it is not employment for the same kinds of people. Similarly, building, installing, and maintaining automatic elevators probably create more employment than if all elevators were still using operators and starters; but not for the same people. Even in industries where current construction of automated equipment employs fewer people than would be employed if the automated equipment were manual, it does not follow that automation has caused unemployment, but only that it has changed the occupation distribution of the labor force.

Even in very short periods when specific jobs are automated out of existence there may not be even temporary unemployment. If the economy is at "full" employment, other jobs will be available almost immediately for almost all displaced employees. When some of those automated out of their jobs do go through a period of unemployment, the explanation is almost always something other than automation: that the economy is not at "full" employment, for example, or that people are reluctant to move their homes. The situation of such unemployed is exactly the same as that of people left unemployed by a shift in consumer demand. The problem is not something special to automation, and measures for dealing with it should not be specialized to those who lost their last jobs because of automation.

Accounts of the amount of labor displaced by automation in specific situations are sometimes grossly exaggerated. A utility executive, to illustrate this, reported that in his company new automatic billing equipment and six employees are now doing a job that would require a hundred if it were done by hand. He added, however, that the job had not been done by hand since 1907. The new machines with their six people had replaced other machines with 14 people. Furthermore, besides the six people now at work directly on billing, three had had to be added in other departments solely because of the billing machines. Thus, what at first sounded like a reduction in employment of 94 turned out to be a reduction of 5. Finally, the executive added that of the eight displaced from the billing department, two had withdrawn from the labor force for other reasons, and the other six had been snapped up elsewhere in the same firm.

On the question of what actually happens in technological displacement—how many people are, as a matter of actual experience, unemployed, and for how long, because of automation—there is so little factual knowledge as to be essentially none. Talk about this seems to be, however, in inverse proportion to the amount of knowledge.

*   *   *   *   *   *

Automation and other labor-saving innovations, though they reflect such general cultural characteristics as the stream of technological and scientific progress, are substantially influenced by economic factors. Factors tending to stimulate a high rate of discovery and development of new methods of automation are:

(1) Firms producing automation equipment serve all of industry. This means that they are likely to benefit from almost any results of research that they support; it thus leads them to support more research than would occur if production equipment were designed and produced in the same firms that use it—as are new products.

(2) The development of modern weapons systems has created a great deal of new technology related to control systems, and a large corps of scientists and engineers capable of developing automation.

(3) Industrial research grew at an extraordinarily high rate in the 1950's, thus tending to produce many new labor-saving devices. Probably industrial research will expand more slowly in the late 1960's.

(4) The fact that the amount of capital available is growing faster than the labor force necessarily leads to the development of labor-saving techniques, that is, techniques by which each worker can handle a larger amount of equipment.

Many labor-saving devices that are known may be uneconomical, hence not in use. Any factor that raises the cost of labor relative to that of capital will lead to the introduction of some of the available labor-saving devices that previously were unused. How far the process will go depends on whether the upward pressure on wage rates is relieved as the process of automation approaches the point where labor would be forced into less productive occupations. When the upward pressure on wages is not relieved (that is, when growth in wages outstrips growth in productivity) automation may be carried to an uneconomic extreme, too much capital being drawn into certain industries and too much labor being forced out of them and into other industries. Automation may also be pushed to uneconomic extremes if special tax privileges are granted for new equipment but not old.

The construction of automation equipment tends to raise the overall level of employment—to replace a long future period of employment by a shorter immediate period of higher employment. Opportunities for doing this will not be exhausted in the foreseeable future; indeed, it can be foreseen with considerable confidence that they never will be exhausted. There is, in short, no problem, nor any prospect of ever having a problem, of general unemployment due to automation.

Any problems of unemployment connected with automation are, like problems of unemployment connected with shifts in demand, problems of the distribution of the labor force.

Ewan Clague and Leon Greenberg

7

Employment

One of the great economic debates of the past few years has been over the issue of whether it is insufficient aggregate demand or structural labor force change which is responsible for the recent high levels of unemployment. Each of these is undoubtedly present—in different degrees at different times. Over the long run, technological change and increased productivity have contributed to growth of the economy and to expansion of employment opportunities. In the short run, however, numerous dislocations occur, requiring transfer and adjustment of workers to new occupations or new industries. If this shift of workers from an old to a new activity is slow and inefficient, the economy as well as the worker is penalized. The consequence of such inefficiency is loss of income and of output. In this sense, at least, structural change is a contributor to unemployment.

So, from an economic point of view, it is sound policy to assist workers in their process of re-adjustment to technological change. Nor can we overlook the social implications. For some workers, the transition to a new kind of job is feasible, but for others the process may be painful, demoralizing, and seemingly beyond their individual capabilities.

Technological change has labor force implications not only in terms of displacement and adjustment, but also for those new workers who are or will be preparing for a vocation and who will begin their job hunting sometime in the future. Changing technology means new industries and new kinds of jobs which may require different skills than those of the past.

Ewan Clague *is Commissioner of Labor Statistics;* Leon Greenberg *is Chief of the Division of Productivity and Technological Developments, Bureau of Labor Statistics, U. S. Department of Labor. Some of the figures presented here are based on unpublished data and are not to be regarded as official estimates of the Bureau of Labor Statistics. The views expressed are those of the authors and not necessarily those of the Department of Labor.*

All of these factors have implications for the workers as individuals and for organized labor, management, the community, and the government. In turn, they have implications for programs of unemployment insurance, placement services, apprenticeship, employer training programs, union organization, educational curricula, and adult education. Inadequacies which might exist in such programs would contribute to the inefficient allocation of manpower.

With this as background, we propose to examine several aspects of the relationship of technological change to employment. We will use productivity (output per man or man-hour) as the indicator of, or guide to, the rate of technological change, recognizing that productivity is affected by many factors, including the skill and education of the work force, capital investment, managerial ability, capacity utilization, and others. Productivity may be expressed as output per man-hour or, in reverse, as man-hours per unit of output (labor requirements). We can produce more goods (and services) with the same labor, or the same output with less labor. In statistical terms, these two expressions mean the same thing; but the former implies economic growth, while the other implies unemployment.

Analysis of these trends—in productivity and employment—over short time periods of four years or less may introduce factors, such as the business cycle, which may obscure the technological factor. The choice of a very long time period results in the introduction of other social, economic, and political variables which may also obscure the displacement impact of technology. Since we are concerned with the unemployment problems which have arisen in recent years, the analysis concentrates on the postwar period (or parts of it). However, since some questions have arisen regarding acceleration (or lack of it) in productivity, this paper includes some comparisons of recent and past trends.

The picture is also blurred when analysis is confined to the economy as a whole, or to major sectors alone. The aggregate approach, while useful and sometimes the only alternative available, may average out hundreds of individual events. Technological change does not occur uniformly and evenly throughout the economic system. Indeed, there are sharp break-throughs in some industries or some production processes while others remain dormant. Technology spreads by differential advantage, even within an industry. So its consequences, for economic growth or for unemployment, must be studied in detail.

If the rate of productivity increase were to match the rate of increase in output, plant by plant, industry by industry, there would be no net displacement of workers, and increments to unemployment could be attributed entirely to lack of growth of demand or output. (But even here, technological change would mean job displacement within the plant as the nature of work shifted from one kind of occupation to another.)

The facts are that changes in productivity are not perfectly correlated with changes in output. But, industry by industry, have productivity gains been accompanied by employment declines or employment increases? Has there been some industrial pattern to the behavior of productivity and employment or has it been generally random?

In order to throw some light on these questions, we have examined the relationship of productivity and employment for sectors of the economy and individual industries in manufacturing in the postwar period.

Finally, technological change may result in various kinds of displacement and re-employment problems, within plants as well as among industries, as the nature of work shifts from one kind of skill or occupation to another. The third part of this paper deals with some of the occupational implications of technological change.

PRODUCTIVITY TRENDS

This analysis will be brief because the subject has been covered fairly extensively in other literature[1] and because of reasons explained in the next section.

There is little question that the average over-all rate of increase in output per man-hour in the postwar period has been greater than the average increase for the long-run period. The postwar (1947-61) average annual increase is 3 to 3.3 per cent (depending on the source of man-hour data), while the long-run (1909-61) average is 2.4 per cent. If we eliminate what some regard as the unusual, early postwar recovery boost and deal with the period 1950-61, the rate of increase has also been somewhat higher than the long-run 2.7-2.9 per cent (Table 1).

Lying behind these figures are a number of contributory trends of component industry sectors. The trends for these sectors, both long-run and for subperiods, are affected in different ways by wartime conversion (and peacetime reconversion), by the Depression, and by technological change.

One of the more dramatic trends is shown by agriculture in which technology—mechanization, cultivating techniques, seed, fertilizer and insecticides—combined with a decline in farm population, resulted in a gradual upsweep in output per man-hour. An average annual increase of 1.1 per cent per year in the decade 1919-29 was increased gradually until it reached an average of over 5½ per cent for the postwar period.

In nearly all of the other industry sectors the rate of change in output per man-hour in the postwar period appears to have exceeded the long-run average. For a few like mining, construction, and finance and service the rate was substantially higher.

[1] See, for example, "Trends in Output per Man-Hour in the Private Economy, 1909-1958," Bulletin No. 1249, U. S. Department of Labor, and "Higher Unemployment Rates, 1957-60: Structural Transformation or Inadequate Demand," Subcommittee on Economic Statistics, Joint Economic Committee, U. S. Congress, 1961.

TABLE 1

*Average Annual Change in Output Per Man-Hour[1] in the Total Private
Economy, Agriculture, and Nonagriculture, 1909-61*

	Labor force estimates			Establishment estimates		
Period	Total private	Agriculture	Non-agriculture	Total private	Agriculture	Non-agriculture
1909-61	2.4	2.3	2.1	2.4	2.3	2.1
1919-61	2.7	2.9	2.3	2.6	2.9	2.2
1919-29	2.9	1.1	2.7	2.9	1.1	2.7
1919-23	3.1	1.3	2.8	3.0	1.3	2.8
1923-29	2.0	1.1	1.8	2.0	1.1	1.9
1929-39	2.2	2.0	2.1	2.2	2.0	2.1
1939-47	2.9	1.5	2.3	2.9	1.5	2.3
1947-61	3.3	5.7	2.7	3.0	5.7	2.4
1950-61	2.9	5.6	2.4	2.7	5.5	2.2

[1] Covers man-hours of wage and salary workers, self-employed and unpaid family
workers. Annual averages are computed from the least squares trend of logarithms of
index numbers.
Source: Trends in Output per Man-Hour in the Private Economy, 1909-1958, Bull.
No. 1249, and annual extensions, U. S. Department of Labor, Bureau of Labor Statistics.

In most industry sectors the annual increase in output per man-hour
in the decade following World War I (1919-29) also appears to have been
higher than the long-run average, although generally not quite as high as
in the post World War II period (Table 2).

TABLE 2

*Average Annual Change[1] in Output per Man-Hour, Nonagriculture,
by Sector, Selected Periods 1909-53*

Sector	1909-1953	1919-1953	1919-1929	1929-1948	1948-1953
Mining	2.8	3.1	4.3	2.2	4.5
Construction	0.3	0.7	1.0	0.1	2.7
Manufacturing	2.7	3.1	5.6	1.7	3.4
Transportation	3.8	4.0	3.4	4.4	3.5
Communications and public utilities .	3.9	4.0	2.7	4.5	4.5
Trade	1.3	1.6	1.1	1.9	1.4
Finance and service—Total	1.6	1.3	([2])	1.8	2.6
Finance	N.A.	N.A.	N.A.	1.4	0.9
Service	N.A.	N.A.	N.A.	1.8	2.8

N.A.—Not available.
[1] Rates of change computed between terminal years.
[2] Negative.
Source: Based on data from *Productivity Trends in the United States*, Appendix Table
A-XI and Appendix C Tables by John W. Kendrick, National Bureau of Economic
Research, 1961.

In the period of the Depression and World War II the growth of output per man-hour was severely retarded in mining, construction, manufacturing and trade, while the other sectors seem to have shown some improvement over previous trends.

Thus, although the trends among industry sectors have not been uniform, there appears to have been a spurt in productivity growth immediately following both World Wars, with a fairly sharp deceleration in the Depression and a modest slow down in more recent years.

OUTPUT PER MAN-HOUR AND EMPLOYMENT

As indicated in the introduction, we recognize that technological progress and higher productivity are stimuli to the progress of the economy and in the long run create more employment opportunities than they eliminate. The figures on Gross National Product, employment, and productivity, as of now compared with 50 years ago, clearly illustrate the long-run story.

There is no net over-all displacement of labor as long as Gross National Product keeps pace with the gains in output per man-hour.[2] But the technological changes and productivity movements among plants and industries are accompanied by differential movements in output. So, employment displacement may be directly associated with productivity gains, even though there is no net, over-all displacement for the total economy.

The experience of many individual industries indicates the same kind of trend as that for the economy—that is, long-term growth in output, employment, and productivity. However, the relationship among these elements may vary in the short run, creating problems of technological displacement. Therefore, it is useful to examine some of the recent trends in output per man-hour and in employment, to try to determine whether or not productivity gains seem to be associated with employment declines.

The analysis which follows is an examination of the productivity-employment relationship among sectors and industries. We use the term "disemployment" to refer to the decline in employment associated with the increase in productivity (or the decline in unit man-hours). It is assumed that employment decreases accompanied by an equivalent decline in output are not associated with productivity change. This is probably an understatement of the productivity-disemployment relationship because employment reductions in some plants and industries is a direct result of technological substitution, that is, of technological change in competing plants and industries, and of materials and fibers. The re-

---

[2] But unemployment will rise if Gross National Product does not increase fast enough to match the increases in productivity plus the increments to the labor force.

placement of coal by oil, natural fiber by synthetic fiber, rail transportation by the automobile, plastics for metals are good examples of technological substitution.

At the same time, decreases in industry employment do not necessarily mean that workers are laid off and become unemployed. In some cases, employment reductions are achieved through normal attrition—deaths, retirements, and quits.

This analysis is, however, suggestive of the magnitude of the productivity-disemployment relationship and, it is hoped, may indicate some direction for further work in attempting to quantify the problem.

The economy and major sectors

In the post-World War II period, employment and output per man-hour in the total private economy both increased. This holds for the earlier and later parts of the period; from 1947-53 employment rose 7.4 per cent, output per man-hour 24.2 per cent; from 1953-59 employment rose 3.4 per cent, output per man-hour 17.0 per cent (Table 3).[3]

In agriculture large gains in output per man-hour throughout the period were accompanied by fairly large declines in employment, as workers and small farm owners left the farms for more lucrative pay in other industries.

Among the major nonagricultural sectors, three had a lower level of employment in 1959 than in 1953. In two of these (transportation and mining output per man-hour went up more than the average for non-agriculture; in the other (manufacturing) the increase was about average. The sector with the largest gain in output per man-hour (public utilities) showed a slightly less than average increase in employment. Three of the sectors with below-average productivity gains showed increases in employment which were larger than the gains (or losses) in employment experienced by the sectors with higher productivity increases.[4]

The correlation between changes in output per man-hour and employment appears to be low. But it does seem as though there was a slight tendency for large gains in output per man-hour to be associated with declines or small increases in employment, and for smaller gains in output

[3] The year 1953 is used as a convenient dividing point, partly based on availability of certain estimates. Results and conclusions would be roughly the same if another year, say 1955, were used. Years such as 1954 and 1956 are recession years and should be avoided as terminal points. The year 1957 is too recent as a beginning year for analysis of trends.

[4] The figures on output per man-hour for these various sectors are not to be regarded as official estimates of the Bureau of Labor Statistics. They are based partly on data derived from Alterman and Jacobs, extended and revised by Schultz (see Table 3), and are subject to certain statistical limitations.

TABLE 3

*Per cent Change in Employment and Output Per Man-Hour in the
Private Economy and Major Sectors, Selected Periods, 1947-59*

Sector	1947-53		1953-59		1955-59	
	Employ-ment	Output per Man-Hour	Employ-ment	Output per Man-Hour	Employ-ment	Output per Man-Hour
Total Private	7.4	24.2	3.4	17.0	1.9	10.0
Agriculture	−22.8	53.6	−11.0		−13.1	18.1
Nonagricultural				30.7		
Industries	12.9	17.8	5.1	14.6	3.8	8.1
Mining	−8.7	33.3	−14.2	20.2	−7.2	8.8
Construction ...	28.4	12.5	14.3	3.9	6.5	0.9
Manufacturing .	12.8	21.1	−5.2	14.5	−1.4	8.0
Transportation .	−2.0	32.0	−11.4	31.4	−5.9	17.8
Communications and Public Utilities	17.8	32.7	3.6	46.7	1.8	29.9
Trade	12.3	14.3	7.7	11.1	4.9	5.7
Services	13.2	2.5	18.8	10.6	11.7	8.9
Finance and Insurance	30.2	17.8	25.4	14.4	14.5	12.8

Source: Output estimates for the total private economy, agriculture, nonagricultural industries and manufacturing from BLS Bulletin 1249 extended to 1959. Other output estimates based on unpublished data from Charles Schultze, revising and extending his estimates published in "Price, Cost and Output 1947-57", Committee for Economic Development (with some adjustment by the authors). Employment and man-hour data from the Bureau of Labor Statistics. Differences between these estimates and those of Kendrick, in Table 2, are primarily due to differences in industry definition and, in one or two cases, methods of measuring output.

per man-hour to be associated with larger than average gains in employment.

The experience in the 1953-59 period was similar to that of the earlier period 1947-53, when the correlation between productivity gains and employment changes was somewhat smaller. The two sectors with the largest declines in employment (mining and transportation) showed the largest increases in output per man-hour. However, the communications and public utilities sector, which also showed one of the largest increases in output per man-hour, had a rather large increase in employment.

Thus it would appear that there has been no significant correlation, positive or negative, between productivity and employment among the major sectors in the postwar period. However, these sectors are very broad in coverage, and are composed of many individual industries in which diverse, and compensating, movements may have occurred. The following section explores these diverse relationships among the individual industries in the manufacturing sector.

Manufacturing

In order to obtain a general, over-all view of the relationship between employment and productivity among individual industries in manufacturing, we have correlated these variables for two dissimilar (but overlapping) parts of the postwar period. We have compared the change in output per man-hour with the change in employment, industry-by-industry, covering over 200 different industries. A high positive correlation would indicate that productivity was employment creating among industries; that is, the larger the productivity gain the larger the increase in employment. A high negative correlation would indicate disemployment; that is, the industries with larger productivity gains would have employment decreases or smaller employment gains.

In the first decade after the war, 1947-57, total manufacturing employment increased, as did output per man-hour. In the period 1953-59, employment declined and output per man-hour rose, but not as sharply. However, for both periods the detailed industry-by-industry analysis showed very little correlation between employment and output per man-hour.

Various other studies have also shown little correlation between output per man-hour and employment in manufacturing over periods covering several years. Kendrick's analysis for 80 manufacturing industries indicates a slightly negative correlation in the period 1948-53, but the ratio is too small to be significant. His study also shows a positive correlation of 0.33 over the long run 1899-1953, and although this is a low correlation ratio he concludes: "Apparently, the theoretical propositions that prices tend to equal unit costs and that industries with declining relative unit costs tend to enjoy increases in relative demand and output describe the operations of the real economy more aptly if a rather long period is allowed for the adjustments to take place." [5]

An analysis by Fabricant for the years 1899-1937, covering the total period and subperiods within, also shows very little correlation among industries between changes in output per man-hour and employment.[6]

These low correlation ratios show that, on the average, productivity gains among industries are associated with both increases and decreases in employment over a period of years. Put another way, and consistent with the point made earlier in this paper, employment decreases occur in industries with large productivity gains and those with small (or no) productivity gains. In the latter case, the declines in employment are obviously closely associated with the decreases in output.

[5] John W. Kendrick, *Productivity Trends in the United States.*
[6] Solomon Fabricant, "Employment in Manufacturing, 1899-1939 (An Analysis of Its Relation to the Volume of Production)," National Bureau of Economic Research, Inc., No. 41, New York, 1942.

But, again, this over-all correlation analysis obscures the impact of technological and employment changes occurring among the several hundred industries within manufacturing. In the period 1953-59, total employment declined by about 880,000 or 5 per cent, while man-hours per unit of output (the inverse of output per man-hour) of all employees declined by a greater amount.[7] So, it might be said that all of the employment decline was associated with the decline in unit man-hours (i.e., with the increase in productivity). On the other hand the correlation ratio does not show a significant relationship. Can we learn something more by a detailed examination of individual industries? Can we make some estimate of the magnitude of the displacement figure and identify the industries in which displacement occurs?

For this detailed analysis, estimates of unit man-hours were derived for 201 industries in manufacturing[8] and related to employment changes from 1953 to 1959 (Table 4). The 201 industries employed nearly 12½ million workers in 1953, representing about 70 per cent of total manufacturing. The industries were divided into two broad groups—those with employment decreases and those with employment increases. For the latter group there is, of course, no net loss in employment associated with productivity gains. (Although there may have been such an association among individual plants in the industry.)[9]

The industries with employment decreases were divided into three subgroups:

1. Those with an increase in unit man-hours. The decrease in employment was not associated with unit man-hours but was associated entirely with a decline in output.
2. Those where the per cent decrease in unit man-hours equaled or exceeded the per cent decrease in employment. The entire decrease in employment is associated with the decrease in unit man-hours.
3. Those where the per cent decrease in unit man-hours was less than the per cent decrease in employment. Part of the employment decline is disemployment—that part which is equivalent to the decline in unit man-hours.

Employment in the 201 sample industries declined by 775,000. The disemployment figure (decline in employment associated with decline in unit man-hours) was less than this—596,000. Applying these figures to total manufacturing yields a total disemployment estimate of about 745,-000 employees between the terminal years of the six-year period 1953-59.

[7] Similar trends would appear if 1955 were taken as a starting point. However, 1955-59 would be too short a period for this type of analysis. Data for 1960 and 1961 are not yet available for many industries.

[8] These detailed estimates are subject to some margin of error.

[9] To a certain extent the relationship between unit man-hour and employment changes is affected by changes in annual hours worked, but on the average this was not significant during this period.

TABLE 4

Relationship between Changes in Employment and Changes in Unit Man-Hours, All Employees, Manufacturing, 1953-59

Type of Industry	Number of industries	Employment (000's)		Change in employment			
				Total		Associated with unit man-hours	
		1953	1959	Actual (000's)	Per cent	Actual (000's)	per cent
Industries with decline in employment							
Decrease in unit man-hours equaled or exceeded decrease in employment	58	4,023	3,737	−286	−7.1	−286	−7.1
Decrease in unit man-hours was less than total decrease in employment	55	2,860	2,203	−657	−23.0	−309	−10.8
Unit man-hours increased	21	2,072	1,784	−288	−13.9		
Industries with increase in employment							
Unit man-hours decreased	56	3,100	3,524	+424	+13.7		
Unit man-hours increased	11	361	394	+33	+9.1		
Total—sample industries	201	12,413	11,642	−773	−6.2	−595	−4.8
Total manufacturing ..		17,029	16,059	−970	−5.7	−745	−4.3

Source: Derived from unpublished estimates based on Census production and employment data.

There was, apparently, no special pattern to the 113 industries of disemployment. All types of industries experienced this employment-unit man-hour relationship—durables and nondurables, food, textiles, metalworking, machinery, etc. They included small and large industries, ranging from those which had fewer than 5,000 employees to those with over 500,000 in 1953.

The 88 industries in which there was no disemployment, including those with employment increases and those where the employment decreases were associated entirely with decreased output, also varied. They included durables and nondurables, cutting across almost all of the 2-digit industry groups, and ranged from small to large.

A striking illustration of the nature of the displacement problem shows up when the detailed employment and unit man-hour analysis is applied to production workers (Table 5). Of the 201 sample industries, there were 135 in which there was a decline of 820,000 production workers associated

TABLE 5

Relationship between Changes in Employment and Changes in Unit Man-Hours, Production Workers, Manufacturing, 1953-59

Type of Industry	Number of industries	Production workers (000's)		Change in production workers			
				Total		Associated with unit man-hours	
		1953	1959	Actual (000's)	Per cent	Actual (000's)	Per cent
Industries with decline in production workers							
Decrease in unit man-hours equaled or exceeded decrease in employment	80	4,915	4,393	−522	−10.6	−522	−10.6
Decrease in unit man-hours was less than decrease in employment	55	2,904	2,178	−726	−25.0	−298	−10.3
Unit man-hours increased	14	291	225	−66	−22.7		
Industries with increase in production workers							
Unit man-hours decreased	45	1,789	2,055	+266	+14.9		
Unit man-hours increased	7	138	155	+17	+12.2		
Total—sample industries	201	10,037	9,006	−1,031	−10.3	−820	−8.2
Total manufacturing ..		13,683	12,260	−1,423	−10.4	−1,131	−8.3

Source: Derived from unpublished estimates based on Census production and employment data.

with decreases in unit man-hours. This yields an estimate of 1,131,000 production workers for total manufacturing for the period 1953-59, or nearly 200,000 per year. Thus, disemployment accounted for about 80 per cent of the total decline in production-worker employment. This ratio was very close to that for all employees (77 per cent). However, it is obvious that the disemployment figure for production workers (1,131,000) was substantially higher than that for all employees (745,000).[10]

As with the all-employee analysis, there was no particular industrial pattern to the employment and unit man-hour relationships for production workers. Various kinds of industries were represented in the different groups and they varied in size.

The disemployment figures associated with declines in unit man-hours do not account for the total production worker decline which occurred between 1953 and 1959. The remainder, about 682,000 (or 114,000 per year), occurred in industries in which decreased employment was associated with decreased output. This figure was about two-thirds as high as that for the productivity associated disemployment.

Is it possible to use the results of this analysis to predict the magnitude of the technological displacement problem in the coming decade? We are aware of the perils of prediction, but we think the figures are useful as an indicator of magnitudes—as suggestive of the size of the displacement problems that may lie ahead.

We have seen that in the period 1953-59, there was disemployment of 1,131,000 production workers in manufacturing, or about 200,000 per year. But this was a period during which output showed very little gain while over-all employment declined. Would similar results be obtained in a period of expanding output and rising employment? For this purpose, an additional, similar analysis has been prepared for the period 1947-57, when output rose over 40 per cent and employment of production workers increased about 1½ per cent (Table 6).

Estimates for 313 industries were derived for the 1947-57 period. Out of this total, 153 of them showed disemployment of 876,000 production workers in the 1947-57 period, or 7.3 per cent of the nearly 12 million workers they employed in 1947. For total manufacturing the figure would be roughly 883,000 production workers, or nearly 90,000 per year. At the same time, there was a decline of about 228,000 production workers (23,000 per year) associated with decreases in industry output. In other words, even in a period of rapidly rising output, accompanied by an increase in employment for total manufacturing, there were many industries in which there was a decline in employment associated with declines in unit man-hours or, to a much lesser extent, with decreases in output. The relationship between changes in unit man-hours and employment increases or decreases was scattered among many industries throughout manufacturing, so again there was no particular industrial pattern to the disemployment figures.

Thus, we have two estimates of employment decreases associated with

[10] This does not mean that output per man-hour or unit man-hour indexes for production workers are superior in any general sense to those for all employees, or vice versa. It is, however, an indication of the usefulness of various kinds of productivity measures for manpower analysis.

TABLE 6

Relationship between Changes in Employment and Changes in Unit Man-Hours, Production Workers, Manufacturing, 1947-57

| | | Production workers (000's) | | Change in production workers | | | |
| | Number of indus- tries | | | Total | | Associated with unit man-hours | |
Type of Industry		1947	1957	Actual (000's)	Per cent	Actual (000's)	Per cent
Industries with decline in production workers							
Decrease in unit man-hours equaled or exceeded decrease in production workers	97	4,289	3,733	−556	−13.0	−556	−13.0
Decrease in unit man-hours was less than decrease in production workers	56	1,636	1,119	−517	−31.6	−320	−19.6
Unit man-hours increased	10	109	78	−31	−28.7		
Industries with increase in production workers							
Unit man-hours decreased	137	5,112	6,849	+1,737	+34.0		
Unit man-hours increased	13	845	955	+110	+13.0		
Total—sample industries	313	11,991	12,733	+742	+6.2	−876	−7.3
Total manufacturing ..		12,092	12,842	+750	+6.2	−883	−7.3

Source: Derived from unpublished estimates based on Census production and employment data.

decreases in unit man-hours. The average annual rate is nearly 200,000 for the period 1953-59 and nearly 90,000 for the period 1947-57. It is generally expected that during the next decade the economy will grow at a faster pace than it has in recent years, but that output per man-hour will also increase more rapidly. If the same expectation is applied to manufacturing, it does not appear unreasonable that there will be disemployment of at least 100,000 production workers in that sector each year, on the average. An additional reduction can be expected in industries where the declines in employment are more directly related to decreases in output.

It has not been possible to perform a similar analysis for the nonmanufacturing sector. Detailed data on output or employment, or for matching the two, are not available for many industries. We do know that, on the whole, employment and output have increased more than in manufacturing, while output per man-hour has increased less. On the other hand, there are nearly twice as many workers in nonmanufacturing as in manufacturing, so the magnitude of disemployment might be on the same order as that for manufacturing.

Summary

The previous analysis indicates that disemployment—decreases in employment associated with increased productivity—in nonagricultural industries might amount to 200,000 workers or more per year during the next decade. It is important to restate that these figures do not tell the whole story, but they suggest an order of magnitude and indicate the kind of exploration that might be made in further attempts to quantify the volume of technological displacement or disemployment.

The figures obtained through this analysis do not necessarily mean that all the disemployed workers became unemployed—some may have quit, retired or died. On the other hand, the figures do not reflect the disemployment that may arise between plants within an industry, nor the replacement and reshuffling that may occur within plants where technological changes are taking place. The figures do not reflect the disemployment arising out of technological competition—where plants may decrease employment or even shut down because they transfer activities to another modern plant, nor do they reflect the impact of technological substitution where plants or industries lose markets to technologically progressive competitors, to new products, and to new materials.

To a certain extent the declines in employment associated with falling output (23,000 per year, 1947-57, over 110,000 per year, 1953-59) include the factors of technological competition and substitution. All decreases in employment could be regarded as technological displacement on the grounds that all changes in the structure of output (and consequently all decreases in output and employment)[11] stem from technological change, since it is the latter which results in substitution of materials and products as well as in new processes. On the other hand, all displacement might be regarded as arising out of insufficient growth in demand and resultant output. This seems to ignore the fact that there will be structural changes in the economy as we progress and that individual establishments or industries cannot be expected to maintain their levels of employment indefinitely.

Nevertheless, from the point of view of the over-all economy, output

[11] Within the context of generally rising output of goods and services and except for increasing foreign competition.

must have the capacity to absorb all those who wish to participate as members of the labor force. In this sense, Gross National Product must grow enough to take care of the nearly 3,000,000 jobs accounted for annually by the over-all growth in productivity plus the new entrants to the labor force.

AUTOMATION AND JOB SKILLS

The preceding analysis has dealt with the net employment effects of technology and productivity—that is, with employment gains or losses among industries. But within plants and industries many technological changes are going on which alter job content—creating new jobs and making some obsolescent. What is the nature of changing job requirements and opportunities and what can we do to prepare for them?

We already know about the long sweep of industrial-occupational changes that have occurred in the last 50 years. The farm is no longer a job haven for millions of persons—including workers and proprietors—who might return to the farm during periods of unemployment and wait until business conditions improved. Farm employment has dropped to the point where it now takes care of only a small per cent of the labor force.

Within the nonagricultural labor force (private and public) a combination of technology and shifts in demand has resulted in a decline in the relative importance of mining and manufacturing employment. The group of transportation, communications, and public utilities industries has declined in importance as the use of private autos has increased and as technological change has lowered labor requirements in the telephone, railroad, airline, and other industries. During this same half century, contract construction, trade, service, and government have all increased their share of employment (Table 7).

All this adds up to a long-term shift from blue-collar to white-collar type of employment. As a consequence—if not also as a cause—more women are employed, and educational requirements for prospective job seekers have gone up.

By and large, these changes in the relative importance of the goods and service sectors are not the result of sudden break-throughs in recent years. The changes appear to be a cumulation of long-term, gradual shifts in the structure of the economy. It is not unlikely that these trends will continue, with modifications. However, it is to be noted that they are the result of differential movements in both output and productivity, so future movements of the employment figures will be affected by both factors.

Technological change has resulted in another kind of employment shift —the declining ratio of production workers to total employment. The shift in manufacturing, as indicated in the previous section, dropped pro-

TABLE 7

Employment by Sector as Per cent of Total Nonagricultural
Employment, Selected Years 1919-60

Industry Sector	1919	1929	1939	1949	1953	1959	1960
Nonagriculture—Total	100.0	100.0	100.0	100.0	100.0	100.0	100.0
Mining	4.2	3.5	2.8	2.1	1.7	1.4	1.3
Contract construction	3.8	4.8	3.8	4.9	5.2	5.5	5.3
Manufacturing	39.3	34.1	33.6	33.0	34.9	31.2	30.8
Transportation, public							
utilities, communication ..	13.7	12.5	9.6	9.1	8.5	7.5	7.4
Wholesale and retail trade ..	16.7	19.5	21.0	21.2	20.4	20.8	21.0
Finance, insurance, real							
estate	4.1	4.8	4.8	4.2	4.3	4.9	4.9
Service and miscellaneous ..	8.4	11.0	11.5	12.0	11.7	13.3	13.5
Government	9.9	9.8	13.0	13.4	13.2	15.3	15.7

Source: Employment and Earnings Statistics in the United States, 1909-60 (BLS Bull. 1312).

duction workers from 82 to 75 per cent of all employees. A similar shift has taken place in mining where production workers have dropped from 90 to 80 per cent of total employment. In contract construction, the other sector for which data are available, production worker employment increased in the postwar period, but not as fast as total employment, and has dropped from 89 to 85 per cent of the total. These trends reflect the shift from blue-collar to white-collar type of employment (Table 8).

TABLE 8

Production Workers as Per Cent of All Employees in Mining, Manufacturing,
and Contract Construction for Selected Years, 1949-60

(in thousands)

Industry	1949	1953	1959	1960
Mining:				
All employees	930	866	731	709
Production workers	839	765	589	567
Per cent of all employees	90.2	88.3	80.6	80.0
Manufacturing:				
All employees	14,441	17,549	16,667	16,762
Production workers	11,790	14,055	12,596	12,562
Per cent of all employees	81.6	80.1	75.6	74.9
Contract construction:				
All employees	2,165	2,623	2,955	2,882
Production workers	1,919	2,305	2,535	2,458
Per cent of all employees	88.6	87.9	85.8	85.3

Source: Employment and Earnings Statistics in the United States, 1909-60 (BLS Bull. 1312).

The unemployment statistics also show the less favorable position of the blue-collar worker. The highest rate of unemployment exists among those who are unskilled, the lowest rates among the skilled and white-collar workers.

But these are broad generalities. How can we better prepare for job needs which will arise in the next 5 to 10 years? Will clerical employment requiring only a high school education be as plentiful as it is now or will office workers need specialized skill training or higher education, or both? Will semi-skilled workers—operatives—find plenty of employment opportunities, as they did in the expansion of the 1920's?

The Bureau of Labor Statistics has made projections of the occupational distribution of the labor force as it is expected to look in 1970. These projections indicate that the proportion of service workers in the labor force will rise slightly. The proportion of farm workers will continue to decline. There will be some increases in relative job opportunities for skilled workers, a slight decline for semi-skilled workers, and a sharp decline for unskilled workers. The importance of white-collar workers will increase; but within this latter group the most rapid rate of increase will be among professional, technical, and kindred workers.

The conclusion is fairly clear. There will be fewer and fewer job opportunities for the unskilled. Many workers with some skill will need to be retrained for different jobs and a higher proportion of workers will need the higher educational attainment required for employment in white-collar occupations.

The Bureau is currently reviewing these projections and they may be revised somewhat—but probably not substantially. There are some technological developments which seem to be spreading very rapidly—more so than had been anticipated only a few years ago. The electronic computer, for example, is making rapid inroads in banks, insurance companies and other industries, including government, where large numbers of clerical workers are employed.

The implications of computer operations could be very serious for a particular group of job seekers—young women who have for many years found employment as clerical workers. Moreover, the computer is capable of performing operations which in the past have required a high degree of clerical or semi-professional skill and may thus also reduce job opportunities for family breadwinners normally employed in these occupations. Of course, against this must be balanced the increased need for programmers and systems analysts. So, while total job opportunities in this area may not decline, there may be great need for training or retraining for new kinds of occupations.

As we indicated earlier, in certain respects it does not matter too much whether productivity and technological change are occurring faster or only as fast as in the past. The fact is that new technology will change the occupational structure of the economy. Although we are able to make some projections of the general nature of these changes, we do not know enough about them in detail and we must be constantly alerted to new developments as they loom ahead—so that adequate steps may be taken in advance to prepare the labor supply to meet the labor demand.

In order to fulfill these needs, the Bureau of Labor Statistics is embarking on two new fact-finding programs. One is a program of technological outlook studies. The other deals with economic growth and employment opportunities.

The technological outlook studies are designed to throw light on future developments for specific kinds of innovations and for industries throughout the economy—especially the major ones. We are trying to look 3, 5, 10 years ahead—to examine the current status of important developments and in what direction and with what speed their rate of adoption and diffusion appears to be heading. Our concern is not primarily with engineering aspects of the new technologies, but with their manpower implications. So we will be examining their prospective influence on productivity, employment, job obsolescence, and new skill requirements.

Changes in technology embrace not only new processes but also new products and new materials. All of these three developments may affect the inputs of different industries and the input-output coefficients among the various industries in the economy. These changes in the production coefficients, in turn, have an effect on the manpower coefficients and, consequently, on future manpower requirements. Therefore, in its studies of technological outlook the Bureau will also explore the changes in material and capital inputs.

The specific application of this latter type of information will be carried out under the Bureau's new studies of economic growth. In this program, alternative projections of Gross National Product, of investment and of demand will be evaluated in terms of their effect on the industry structure of the economy, using input-output techniques. Coefficients of production, capital and manpower emanating from the alternative projections will be determined. In this way a more complete, analytical framework of manpower demand—and the implication for labor force adjustments—will become available.

Richard N. Cooper

8

International Aspects

A most striking feature of the world economy today is the tremendous variation among countries—and even within countries—in the modernity of applied technology. We can find such sharp contrasts as multi-horsepowered electric water pumps and the ancient well-bucket; huge crawler tractors turning ten furrows at a time and the trustworthy ox plowing one skimpy groove; mechanically-powered spinning machines with thousands of spindles and the old foot-powered spinning wheel; large automatic washing machines and the time-tested scrubbing board.

The continuing coexistence of ancient and modern methods of production is due to many factors, but three are of special interest to the economist. First, modern methods usually require large—sometimes enormous—amounts of capital. Second, to be profitable, modern methods frequently require a larger scale of production than can be supported by the market for goods and services. Finally, effective use of modern technology requires a high degree of technical knowledge and vocational skill in the working population, plus a willingness and ability to adapt readily to continually changing vocational requirements.

RICHARD N. COOPER *is on the staff of the President's Council of Economic Advisers. He has been a consultant to the Anti-Trust Division of the Department of Justice and has taught economics at the London School of Economics and the University of Maryland. Dr. Cooper has written on a number of economic problems, including the United States competitive position in world markets. The views in this paper are his own and do not necessarily represent those of the Council of Economic Advisers.*

The rewards of up-to-date technology are high. Modern techniques of production and distribution have raised labor productivity enormously. By so doing they have raised living standards from subsistence levels to the "affluence" enjoyed by most Americans, and at the same time permitted an ever-shorter working week and increased leisure time. The very sharp increases in productivity over the past two centuries are difficult for us to imagine; but we can gain some appreciation of the advantages of modern technology by comparing present living standards in the United States with the lower levels in Europe and with the abysmal poverty which continues to exist in many other regions of the world.

While international comparisons of productivity defy exact measurement, it is broadly correct to say that productivity in the United States today is two to four times higher than in Europe, and it exceeds ten times the productivity levels in many other parts of the world. In a world in which "missile gaps" and "GNP gaps" have become common parlance, we may appropriately speak of a "productivity gap" among countries. To take but a single example, in 1959 the average American worker in manufacturing produced in one hour goods valued at $3.90, while his Japanese counterpart produced only $.40 worth. A part of these substantial international differences in productivity is due to factors other than applied technology. The amount of capital available to each worker, the abundance or scarcity of natural resources, and the skill, education, and "working spirit" of the labor force all contribute to labor productivity. But differences in applied technology remain a crucial determinant of the wide differences in productivity among countries.

The next few decades will almost certainly bring a substantial narrowing of the productivity gap. Capital in the world at large is becoming more abundant, and through quickening foreign aid and international investment it is moving more readily from the regions with a relative abundance to those with a relative scarcity. Growing markets will make techniques of mass production more suitable in many countries which previously could not take advantage of the economies inherent in such techniques. The formation of customs unions, and especially of the European Common Market, will hasten this process. Finally, interest in technological improvements in production methods and a willingness to adopt new methods have spread widely and rapidly. This is true not only for the less developed countries, with their eagerness for rapid industrialization, but also for the European countries, whose interest in United States production methods was stimulated during the period of "dollar shortage" in the early 1950's.

None of these developments is new. What is new is the very rapid pace at which capital and technical knowledge have recently been moving across international boundaries and the accelerated rate at which they can be expected to move in the future.

Some implications for the United States

Technological change within the United States has important effects on work and leisure, labor and management, costs and demand. Technical change abroad, through foreign trade, can similarly affect life in the United States. In 1961 the United States exported over $20 billion in merchandise and imported nearly $15 billion. Merchandise exports accounted for 8 percent of total United States output of goods. The Department of Labor has estimated that 3.1 million American jobs—nearly 6 percent of the total—depend directly or indirectly on exports. The level and composition of imports also vitally affect American production and employment.

The character of United States trade depends intimately on the high level of American productivity, on technology, and on continuing technological change. This is true not only of the obvious cases where technological advance takes the form of new and better export products—such as jet planes, electronic computers, high-speed office machinery, and modern drugs—but also when new technology makes possible economies in the production process—as in the case of poultry, hybrid corn, and other agricultural products.

The great importance of modern technology to the United States trade position has led some economists to contend that America's comparative advantage in world markets lies precisely in those industries in which technical change is especially prevalent. The United States is alleged to have relied to an extraordinary degree in the past on the export of new products and products made with new production techniques. Eventually other countries, with their lower labor costs, adopt the new techniques or start manufacturing the new products themselves, but by that time American producers have moved on to still newer products and newer techniques.

In the early 1950's this hypothesis provided the basis for theories of a lasting "dollar shortage" in the rest of the world; lately the gradual reduction of this technological lead has become a popular explanation for the ailing United States balance of payments position. While this view gives an exaggerated importance to technological change—and underplays the high level of productivity attributable to the advanced *level* of applied technology, to the economies of mass production, to the large capital stock and abundant natural resources, and to trained manpower in the United States—there is no denying that continuing technological change has lent particular strength to the United States foreign trade position.

Will a gradual reduction of the "productivity gap" in the next decade challenge the strong export position of the United States? What impact on United States exports and imports would result from a rise in average

European productivity from one-third to, say, one-half of the United States productivity level? Will the United States find it more difficult to export its products at going prices, while imports enter the large United States market at an accelerating pace? To what extent will formation of the European Common Market and other economic unions hasten the growth in productivity abroad?

Answers to such questions are especially important today because of the large deficits which the United States has recently run in its international payments. These deficits, averaging $3.4 billion annually in the period 1958-1961, were due to many factors and were only partly connected with merchandise trade. The deficits were financed both by selling gold to foreigners and by foreign accumulation of dollar claims against the United States. Payments deficits of such size cannot be run indefinitely without damaging confidence in the dollar as an international reserve currency. If United States payments deficits are to be reduced without jeopardizing our foreign aid and military commitments and without abandoning our traditional policy of freedom for international capital flows, the merchandise trade surplus must be increased accordingly. Any reduction in the international productivity gap resulting in rising living standards abroad should be applauded. But in the interests of maintaining a stable and efficient system of international payments based on the dollar as a reserve currency, the gap must be reduced in ways consistent with an improvement in the United States trade position.

This chapter suggests approximate answers to these crucial questions. The next section provides an indication of existing international differences in productivity. The sections which follow set out the factors which may be expected in the next decade to raise productivity abroad more rapidly than in the United States, and the subsequent sections then examine the effects which closing the productivity gap will have on United States trade.

International comparisons of productivity

Accurate measurement of "productivity," or simply total output per man-hour, is notoriously difficult. International comparisons suffer all the usual problems and many more. This is not the place for an excursus on the technical problems involved, but three reservations about aggregate productivity comparisons among countries can be mentioned.

The first concerns comparability of the underlying data in their definition of coverage and accuracy of recording. Is the part-time seamstress working at home defined as part of the labor force or not? If she is, is she actually counted? Since the amount of part-time and family work varies widely from country to country, differences in concept or errors in measurement can affect substantially the comparability of the final measurements. International data comparisons encounter many pitfalls of this sort. The statistical divisions of various international organizations have made noteworthy progress in achieving uniformity in definitions and accuracy of measurement, but there is still a long way to go.

The second reservation concerns how the varying components of output in each country should be added up. The composition of output and the structure of prices may differ widely between two countries. The total value of output in a foreign economy may be far different when valued in United States prices (converted at official exchange rates) than when valued in its own prices. Goods and services which are cheap and abundantly produced in another country may be relatively scarce and expensive in the United States; they add more to the value of output if measured in high United States prices rather than low foreign prices. For other goods and services the opposite is true, but the two tendencies may not be fully offsetting.

The third problem concerns how to convert the total output in different countries into comparable units. The output of the Italian worker is valued in lire and he is paid in lire; the output of an American worker is valued in dollars. True, there is an international rate of exchange between dollars and lire: one dollar can normally purchase about 620 lire. But exchange rates are determined by many factors other than the productivity and price levels of different economies, so use of a country's official exchange rate to convert output valued in its currency into another currency may systematically over- or understate its productivity.

Despite these reservations, it is instructive to get a rough idea of the size of the productivity gap. The data shown in Table 1 confirm the wide gap in productivity between the United States and Europe, and suggest an even wider gap between the United States and other parts of the world (e.g., Japan). It is noteworthy that the level of wages from country to country is closely related to the level of productivity.

NARROWING THE PRODUCTIVITY GAP

Three factors have been mentioned as tending to narrow productivity between the United States and other countries in the coming decade: rapid diffusion of old and new technology; increased opportunities for economies of scale both in production and in industrial research; and high rates of capital formation abroad. These are not, of course, three separate and additive factors. There is an important interaction, for example, between the rate of investment and the ability to achieve economies of large scale production. New investment is also an important carrier of technical change. Similarly, economies of scale and improvements in applied technology are frequently complementary. But it is nonetheless useful to focus attention on each of these factors separately.

TABLE 1

International Differences in Productivity and Wages
(in U.S. Dollars)

	Gross National Product per Man-year of Employment, 1960		Net Output per Man-hour in Manufacturing, 1959[b]	Hourly Earnings in manu-facturing, 1959[bc]
	Converted at Official Exchange Rates	Adjusted for Price Difference[a]		
United States	7,330	7,330	3.89	2.68
Western European countries combined	2,270	——	——	——
European Common Market	2,510	——	——	——
Belgium	3,480	4,590	1.33	.74
Canada	6,090	n.a.	2.56	1.89
France	2,940	3,500	n.a.	.71
Germany, F.R.	2,640	4,410	.96	.78
Italy	1,640	3,020	.96[d]	.61
Japan	760[e]	n.a.	.40	.29
Netherlands	2,600	4,470	1.01	.57
Norway	3,000	4,380	1.29	.90
United Kingdom	2,630	3,980	.97	.77

[a] Using conversion factors based on United States price weights computed for 1955 by Milton Gilbert et al., *Comparative National Products and Price Levels*, Paris, 1958.
[b] Converted at official exchange rates.
[c] Including fringe benefits; Canada, Japan, and Norway estimated by the author, others by the French National Institute of Statistics and Economic Studies.
[d] Production workers only.
[e] 1959.

Diffusion of technology

Effective diffusion of existing technical knowledge and the means with which to implement it would result in striking increases in output and productivity abroad. Many countries would "catch up" to the most advanced levels of applied technology. This possibility for catching up to the technically most advanced nations has existed ever since Britain, starting the Industrial Revolution, shed its old methods of production for new ones and became the "workshop of the world." Some countries— Belgium, France, Germany, the United States, and others—did indeed catch up and even surpass Britain in applied technology; but others adhered to traditional techniques of production and only slipped further and further behind as the industrial countries continued to adopt ever new methods.

Recently, however, two important changes have combined to make the international diffusion of technology more rapid and more widespread than before. The first is the newly awakened interest throughout the world in learning and using the latest techniques of production and management. The second is the sharp increase in the outflow of American capital to foreign countries.

Since the Second World War an unparalleled interest has arisen in adopting modern production techniques. Evidence for this lively interest can be seen in the large international exchange of technical missions, such as the European productivity teams which studied United States methods in the early 1950's, and the widespread hiring of American engineers and management consultants by foreign governments and firms. The large number of foreign students in this country also testifies to the great and growing interest in learning advanced production and management techniques. In 1960-1961 there were 53,000 foreign students in the United States, a rise from 30,000 in 1950-1951. The proportion of foreign students studying science, engineering, business, or agriculture rose from 38 percent to 51 percent over the same period.

Study by foreigners in the United States is one way to diffuse technical knowledge; another is for Americans to carry it abroad. Through private overseas investment and government aid this has been occurring at an accelerating pace. The outflow of United States capital for direct investment in American-controlled firms abroad rose from $700 million annually from 1951 to 1955 to an annual average of $1.6 billion in 1956-1961. Large additional investments were made from retained earnings abroad and from borrowing in foreign capital markets. With American investment goes American management and American technology. The more such direct investment occurs, the more rapidly American "know-how" gets transplanted abroad.

We are unlikely in the future to retain for as long as in the past the competitive advantages of new inventions, new products, and new production techniques. The growing popularity of licensing agreements (whereby, for a fixed fee or royalty, American manufacturers extend their technical knowledge and patent rights to foreign producers) assures that new technology will move rapidly to countries where production is advantageous despite the patent monopoly of the inventor. One measure of the rapid growth of licensing and management consulting abroad is the trebling between 1950 and 1960 of royalties and fees received by the United States. Recently the earnings on such "sales of know-how" to foreigners have exceeded $500 million annually.

In sum, the international diffusion of technical knowledge has probably occurred much more rapidly in the recent than in the distant past, and this trend will undoubtedly continue. Foreign interest in new techniques and American interest in operating abroad combine to reduce the "splendid isolation" in applied technology which many feel the United States previously enjoyed.

Economies of scale

Growing markets abroad may provide, in themselves, the basis for reductions in the great international differences in productivity. Costs can frequently be reduced and efficiency raised by increasing the scale of production and sales where limited markets and restrictive business practices now restrict the scale of output below the level permitting efficient use of mass production and distribution techniques. By enlarging the market, both through reduction of trade barriers and through economic growth, these latent increases in productivity can be realized.

The possibility for enlarging markets is most immediately in prospect for the tariff-free European Common Market. Already in the process of forming a market of 170 million consumers with a combined gross national product of $180 billion, the Common Market will increase to 220-250 million consumers and a GNP exceeding $250 billion with the accession of the United Kingdom and others. With total purchasing power (corrected for price increases) equivalent to that in the United States in 1941, the Common Market would permit a scale of production in European firms much larger than at present, perhaps resulting in substantial increases in efficiency. Three areas provide important opportunities for such "economies of scale": mass production, widespread distribution and sales, and enlarged expenditures for research and development of new products and new production techniques.

Mass Production—Economies of scale are usually associated with the introduction of the so-called techniques of mass production. By standardizing and simplifying operations, specializing worker tasks, establishing a well-defined sequence of operations, and lengthening production runs, labor productivity is raised and costs per unit of output reduced. Such techniques often require increasing mechanization of the production process—a fully automated plant carries this to its logical limit—but sometimes sizeable economies can be obtained simply by improved management and a rearrangement of existing machinery and labor tasks, resulting in higher output and less waste.

Economists are divided on whether important economies of scale in production are likely to result from the European Common Market. Some point out that, however small they may be compared with those of the United States, the national markets of Europe are already sufficiently large to permit any significant economies of scale in production in all but a few industries. And foreign markets, already important to the countries of Europe, act as an extension of the domestic market by permitting larger scale production than could be absorbed by national markets alone. The high efficiency of Belgian industry is no doubt partly due to the large scale of operation permitted by the existence of extensive export markets.

Others contend that important economies of scale in production are still possible in Europe. Lack of standardization, unnecessary diversity in finished products, and a fragmentation of markets all conspire to keep production runs short and production techniques inefficient by United States standards. Foreign markets are alleged to have requirements too diverse, demand too uncertain, to permit the steady flow of output required by mass production techniques. Such examples of large scale American production as the Ford engine plants and the huge continuous strip mills are cited as evidence that substantial cost reductions from enlarged output are still available to Europe.

Evidence on the subject is not conclusive, but on balance it points to the possibility of substantial reductions in average costs resulting from increased European output. In his *New Barriers to Competition* Joe Bain estimated that in the United States 600,000 units a year is the most efficient scale of output for any one line of automobiles. At 150,000 units costs are moderately higher and at 60,000 units they are substantially higher. For tractors Bain estimated the optimum output for a firm at 60,000 to 90,000 units a year. Most European auto lines ran fewer than 100,000 units annually in the mid-fifties, and the entire tractor output in France amounted to only 80,000 in 1959. In Sweden it was only 9,000. Because of differences in wages and other costs, the optimum plant size in Europe may be somewhat smaller than in the United States of course; but these figures do suggest the very large output required to make full use of modern production technology.

The smaller scale of output in Europe is frequently due less to the small size of the total market than to the very great diversity of models demanded and produced there. In the mid-fifties France produced 18 types of automobiles and Britain alone produced 48 types, compared with 20 types in the United States. This great diversity shortens production runs and lowers productivity. Even component parts are produced in bewildering variety—45 different electric starters were made by a single firm in Britain—with the resulting high costs but no corresponding benefits from satisfying diverse consumer wants. A careful study of British and American productivity shows American productivity relatively higher in those industries enjoying a substantially greater level of output than their British counterparts.[1]

The possibility for substantial economies of scale seems to be there. But will they be realized? We have perhaps had some foretaste of the latent potentialities for increases in productivity from enlarging the market by experience under the European Coal and Steel Community (ECSC). Before the formation of this limited "common market" in coal and steel products, levels of plant capacity in the European steel industry

---

[1] Deborah Paige and Gottfried Bombach, *A Comparison of National Output and Productivity of the United Kingdom and the United States,* Paris, Organization for European Economic Cooperation, 1959.

were generally too low to benefit fully from modern steel production technology. A United Nations group estimated in 1949 that the optimum capacity for a continuous strip mill was 1.3 million tons of steel annually. Bain places the optimum for an integrated steel plant in the United States at 1.0 to 2.5 million tons annually. Before the establishment of the ECSC European plant capacity was typically far below these levels. Of nine new strip mills immediately antedating the ECSC, only two were of optimum size.

Since 1953, however, a number of substantially larger plants have been installed. In the same period, European steel prices rose far less than American steel prices, despite a continuing high demand for steel. While the causes for this are various, cost-reducing increases in European scale of production may have played an important role in keeping prices lower abroad.

Greater competition among European producers no doubt also figured in the determination of European steel prices. Some economists hold that economies of scale will come about not so much from enlargement of the market as from the increase in competition resulting from elimination of barriers to trade. Faced with the certainty of competition from foreign firms formerly barred by tariff walls, many European firms will eliminate unnecessary product diversity and move closer to the lowest cost scale and techniques of production.

Distribution and Finance—Even where economies of scale in production are not significant, increased efficiency in distribution, in finance, and in over-all management may be brought about by an enlarged selling market. A larger market can lead to substantial economies in marketing differentiated and durable products. The high overhead costs of extensive sales and servicing departments can be spread over a larger volume of goods.

Furthermore, large and well known firms may be able to raise funds cheaper and more easily than small firms, especially as the removal of restrictions on capital flows within the Common Market makes possible borrowing in other member countries. Firms with international reputations will find themselves increasingly able to shop around the capital markets of Europe for credit.

Research and Development—A source for significant economies of scale usually neglected in discussions of the Common Market—but one especially important in discussing technical change—is industrial research and development. Inventive activity has long since ceased to be left to the chance contributions of isolated inventors; large amounts of capital and human skill are being applied in a systematic effort to push outward the frontiers of technology and to turn to practical use basic scientific discoveries already made. By widespread acknowledgment this process has reached its most advanced state in the United States.

Inadequate data prevent fully comparable international comparisons, but research and development expenditures are considerably higher, both absolutely and in relation to GNP, in the United States than in Europe. One study has placed United States research and development expenditures in 1958 at 2.7 percent of GNP, compared with 2.3 percent in the United Kingdom. In other European countries such expenditures are generally under 2 percent of GNP. True, a large part of United States expenditures are undertaken for national defense; but as the example of the jet engine testifies, research and development motivated for military reasons can have important commercial application.

Research expenditures will undoubtedly increase with the formation of an integrated economic union. Larger markets provide the potential sales necessary to justify the high overhead expenditures frequently required to discover and develop new products. Moreover, the high risk of complete failure entailed by any research program can be reduced by diversifying the research in a way open only to large establishments. In the United States 85 percent of industrial research expenditures in 1958 were made by firms with over 5,000 employees; moreover, nearly all large firms *did* research and development, while fewer than 10 percent of the firms employing 100 people or less made research and development expenditures.

Growth of European firms and markets, along with heightened competition within the Common Market, will provide incentives for more industrial research; bringing together scientists and technicians with varying backgrounds may raise the chances that such research will pay off. Scientific progress today has been occurring in such volume and is being published in such scattered places that those involved in research cannot hope to keep abreast of all the latest developments. Technical progress may be furthered significantly by the scientific and technical cross-fertilization which should eventually result from the rise in international mobility of professionals and workers alike within the Common Market.

The returns to expenditures for research and development are difficult to measure, but there is widespread consensus that they are high, both in terms of raising productivity through improvements in production process and in terms of new product development. Rising research expenditures in Europe can thus affect United States trade both by helping raise productivity in Europe and by challenging America's traditional lead in industrial innovation—a lead which in the past has been an important pillar of the strong United States trade position.

Rate of investment

Investment provides the capital on which modern industry depends to complement the skills of labor. Labor productivity can frequently be raised by increasing the average amount of capital per worker. But various studies suggest that such "capital deepening" by itself accounts for only a small part of the historical rise in productivity.[2] New investment nevertheless remains crucial in raising productivity. Technological change rarely occurs in a form allowing mere re-arrangement of existing labor and capital; more often, new techniques require new investment. If the results of technical progress are to be put rapidly to use, the rate of gross investment must generally be high.

We began by observing wide differences in applied technology among countries; but there are also substantial technological and productivity gaps within countries. The diffusion of technical innovation throughout an industry is often a slow process. The automatic loom, invented well before World War I, still accounted in 1946 for only 6 percent of the looms in the United Kingdom. Twenty years after the introduction of cigar-making machines in the United States a quarter of all medium-grade cigars were still handmade. W. E. G. Salter has found (*Productivity and Technical Change*) that labor requirements in the "best practice" plants—usually those embodying the latest techniques—are frequently less than half their average level for the entire industry. A high rate of investment generally increases the diffusion of new technical developments throughout an industry.

In the 1950's the rate of investment in Europe was substantially higher than in the United States. In the period 1955-1960, Germany invested 12 percent of its Gross National Product in new plant and equipment. This investment rate was 16 percent in Norway, 12 percent in the Netherlands, 9 percent in Italy, 8 percent in France, and 9 percent in the western European countries combined, compared with only 6 percent in the United States. Even with higher United States investment rates in the 1960's, some disparity will undoubtedly persist. Geographical shifts in production, the rapidly growing internal market, and the new forces of competition arising from the elimination of intra-European trade barriers will all call for substantial new investment. Some of this investment will not add to the total capital stock, but will merely replace existing capacity as plants in France replace plants in Germany in some lines and vice versa in others. But even such replacement investment raises productivity when the new investment embodies technology more modern than the capacity replaced. Already the Europeans are alleged to have a capital stock considerably "younger" than that in the United States. The outstanding example is Germany, which has largely rebuilt its stock of productive equipment since the Second World War. Continuing high investment engendered by the Common Market will thus hasten the spread of new technology.

[2] See Robert M. Solow, "Technical Change and the Aggregate Production Function," *Review of Economics and Statistics*, August, 1957; and Edward F. Denison, *The Sources of Economic Growth in the United States*, New York, Committee for Economic Development, 1962.

The high dependence of increases in productivity on new investment underlines the importance for growth of high national savings. Here is an important difference between Europe and the less developed countries in the ability to take full advantage of existing technology and of advances in technology. However willing the latter group of countries may be to adopt new methods, a chronic shortage of savings may render them unable to do so. To the extent that aid and private investment from the high income countries fail to make up a deficiency in national savings, the productivity gap between the industrialized and the non-industrialized parts of the world may actually grow while the gap within the industrial world is closing.

The pace of change

It has been argued above that several factors will tend in the next decade to reduce the productivity gap between the United States and Europe—and, it is to be hoped, between the United States and the rest of the world. Do we have any indication how fast these forces will work —how far the gap will be reduced by, say, 1970?

Productivity has been growing more rapidly in Europe and Japan than in the United States for more than a decade (see Table 2). While there is no easy way to separate the various forces operating during the fifties, reconstruction from the Second World War undoubtedly played an important role early in the decade. Europe still had much technological

TABLE 2

Growth in Labor Productivity

(percent per annum)

	Real GNP per Man-year of Employment	
	1950-55	1955-60
United States	2.8	1.5
Western European countries combined	3.7	3.3
European Common Market	4.7	3.8
Belgium	2.6	2.4
Canada	2.9	1.1
France	3.9	3.7
Germany, F.R.	6.2	4.3
Italy	5.4	4.2
Japan	n.a.	7.5[a]
Netherlands	4.1	3.2
Norway	3.3	3.2
United Kingdom	1.9	2.1

[a] 1955-1959.

catching up to do, and national economies had to be reorganized to satisfy the postwar pattern of demand at home and abroad. But European productivity continued to grow rapidly well beyond the reconstruction period.

Whether these high increases in productivity will continue through the 1960's is difficult to say. Reports by returning engineers suggest that the most advanced European firms in many industries have little further to learn from the United States in the way of management and production technology. But there are still untapped increases in productivity through economies of larger scale production, marketing, and research. And there is still a wide gap in technology between the most and the least advanced firms. Under the growing pressures of competition within the Common Market this gap is likely to narrow.

The rate at which the productivity gap between the United States and Europe is reduced depends also, of course, on what happens in the United States. American output per man-hour grew at nearly 3 percent a year in the early fifties, but in the period 1956-1960 the United States economy was relatively sluggish and productivity advanced more slowly. Projecting productivity growth into the future is a hazardous exercise. Many factors—not least of which is the rate at which American manufacturing is automated—will affect the future course of productivity. But a probable range of outcomes provides a useful starting point.

In late 1961 the United States agreed to a target growth in GNP of 50 percent by 1970, set by the 20-nation Organization of Economic Cooperation and Development. This works out to about 4.1 percent a year. Allowing for an annual growth in man-hours worked of 1.5 percent, meeting the OECD growth target would require a productivity increase of 2.6 percent a year. President Kennedy has gone further than the growth target and has stated that a growth rate of 4.5 percent is "well within our capability." This would require an annual increase in productivity of 3.0 percent. Both of these rates are close to the actual increase in American productivity during the early fifties.[3]

A rough estimate of the pace of reduction in the productivity gap can be made by assuming that the difference between the continuing high productivity increases in Europe and a plausible rate for the United States is one percent a year. If the productivity level in the United States is now two and a half times the European level, it would take 23 years for the European level to reach half the United States level, and nearly a century to close the productivity gap entirely. In 1970 American productivity would still be 2.3 times that in Europe. In manufacturing

[3] For a discussion of growth possibilities for the next decade and data on trends in employment and hours, see the *Economic Report of the President*, January 1962, Chapter II. Denison, *op. cit.*, makes some productivity projections to 1980 lower than those suggested here, but the Council of Economic Advisers has implied that a rate of 3.4 percent is possible. *Economic Report, op. cit.*, p. 115.

alone the gap would perhaps close somewhat more rapidly, but even there the period would be longer than is sometimes imagined.

EFFECTS OF NARROWING THE GAP

The prospect for a gradual reduction in the productivity gap between the United States and Europe holds out the possibility for a gradual displacement of American goods from world—and indeed from American —markets. One may ask how can the United States compete with goods produced abroad with the most advanced technology but with hourly labor costs only a fraction of those in the United States? Even its traditional role as the prime source for innovations in products and production techniques may be challenged and sharply curtailed.

Because of its continuing balance of payments difficulties, a weakening competitive position of its products in world markets would, in turn, force the United States to choose among some unpleasant policies to close its international payments deficit. The United States would have to (1) abandon some of its overseas military and foreign aid commitments; (2) impose higher tariffs or direct controls over trade and international payments; (3) deflate the domestic economy; or (4) devalue the dollar. Each of these would have undesirable—perhaps even disastrous—consequences for the international position of the United States and indeed for the healthy survival of the free world.

Higher incomes or lower prices

It does not follow automatically from a rise in productivity abroad, however, that foreign production costs will fall and foreign products will price American goods out of world markets. True, increases in productivity usually open the possibility for lower costs and hence lower prices, since less labor is required for the same level of output. But greater productivity can also be taken in the form of higher incomes for labor and management, thus preventing cost savings from the higher productivity.

In an economy with no dependence on foreign trade, the choice between productivity improvements taken in the form of lower product prices and improvements taken as higher factor incomes depends largely on social preferences regarding the distribution of income. Lower prices benefit all consumers, including such groups on fixed money incomes as pensioners and renters. Higher factor incomes benefit all those involved in current production of goods and services—although those benefits are often distributed unevenly as between, say, factory workers and school teachers. But however the improvement in productivity is taken, desired alterations in the distribution of economic benefits can be taken by off-setting adjustment in the tax structure.

The choice between lower prices and higher incomes makes much more difference for a country involved in foreign trade. Lower prices will raise the competitiveness of its products in world markets; they will displace foreign goods both at home and abroad, raising exports and reducing imports. On the other hand, higher money incomes with no decline in prices will not encourage exports but will generally result in higher imports, thus affecting the trade balance adversely.

In general, some increases in productivity are likely to be taken in higher money incomes, some in lower prices. How these two effects will balance in their impact on American exports cannot be determined *a priori*. But in popular discussion excessive attention has been given to the second factor alone—the cost-reducing implications of rising productivity. We must not forget the income effect. The rise in real incomes made possible by technological advance will probably be taken in higher money incomes rather than in constant earnings with increased purchasing power over lower-priced goods and services. Three factors point in this direction: historical experience, the increasing desire to emulate high American standards of living, and the tight labor market which Europe can be expected to experience during the coming decade.

Historical Experience—It is worth recalling that, historically, the choice between taking increases in living standards made possible by technical progress in the form of higher incomes or lower prices has usually been resolved in favor of higher incomes. Increases in wages have usually followed—or led—gains in productivity. Only during the period 1870-1900 in the United States was there a prolonged decline in the cost of living index. Generally the index was steady or rose, while money incomes rose even faster. Similarly, money incomes in Europe have tended to rise as fast as or faster than the rise in real income permitted by improvements in productivity. (The long downward trend of prices in 19th century Britain may be cited as a major exception.) Since the Second World War this process has continued, rises in money incomes generally outpacing the advances in productivity.

Demonstration Effect—Continuing the historical tendency for money incomes to rise is made more probable by the greatly enlivened interest throughout the world—and not excluding Europe—in higher standards of living. The same improvements in communication which carry United States technical advances abroad also carry a message of living standards never before imagined. There is no doubt much in the American way of life which the typical European can do without; but refrigerators and television sets and packaged food and more travel are all things which will make his life pleasanter—and he knows it. Europe is just entering what Walt Rostow has called the Age of High Mass Consumption.

Moreover, even a slower *growth* in United States living standards can result, for awhile, in a widening *absolute* gap between incomes. With American living standards two to three times those in Europe, the rate of European improvements in productivity would have to be two to three times higher than that in the United States to prevent the difference in real income per capita from increasing for awhile. After a time, of course, the higher growth rate abroad will reduce the difference. In the meantime, ever higher United States living standards set ever higher standards for emulation by those living in other countries.

It is true that higher living standards can be achieved equally with lower prices and no change in money incomes. But a rise in earnings is more visible—there is probably a short-run money illusion—and the very interest in higher living standards will encourage European labor to press its claims for higher wages more vigorously.

Tightening Labor Supply—European labor will be in an especially strong position to negotiate higher wages in the next decade. Outside Italy, unemployment in Europe has been reduced to negligible proportions, and even in Italy it has been dropping sharply. It is noteworthy that while many Americans worry about the loss of jobs due to technological change, the much more rapid increase in productivity abroad has been accompanied by a great reduction, not an increase, in unemployment. In Germany unemployment fell from 1.5 million in 1950 to 230,000 in 1960, even while labor productivity rose about two-thirds. From 1953 to 1960 unemployment fell 20 percent in Italy and 40 percent in Belgium. Continuing high demand seems to be the principal explanation for the remarkable rise in employment, despite ever higher labor productivity.

Projections by the Organization for Economic Cooperation and Development suggest that many European countries will experience a far lower growth in the labor force in the 1960's than was true in the 1950's. An extreme case is illustrated by Germany, where the labor force is expected to grow only 3½ percent in the next ten years, compared with over 16 percent in the past decade. This declining growth in labor supply may be compounded by increasing pressure, urged in the Common Market by France, for a shorter working week.

Finally, vocational and professional training in Europe is not yet geared to provide in sufficient quantity workers with the skills needed for increasingly technical modes of production. Skilled and professional labor is already in very short supply in several countries, and the tradition-bound educational and apprenticeship systems are even slower than those in the United States to adapt to new requirements.

At the same time, rapidly growing populations (more rapidly, on the average, than in the past decade), continuing high rates of investment, and an active interest in raising consumption after two decades of relative deprivation suggest a steady growth in demand for labor. With tight labor markets, European unions can be expected to press wage demands with considerable vigor. Even the highly centralized and policy-conscious unions in countries such as the Netherlands have established a pattern in recent years of requesting, and getting, high wage increases and improvements in working conditions. So long as the international payments positions of the European countries remain strong, public appeals to labor for restraint in wage demands will lack conviction. And continuing tight labor markets should result in increases in earnings even exceeding those negotiated between labor and management—the so-called "wage-drift" which has produced sharp increases in earnings in Sweden and other countries. Finally, the Rome Treaty establishing the Common Market requires an equalization of men's and women's wages in member countries. Outside France, women's wages now average roughly two-thirds of men's wages. This commitment will require an exceptionally rapid rise in women's wages if the gap is to be closed by 1966, as planned.

All these factors, combined with recently established expectations for high annual wage increases, should be sufficient to ensure that technical improvements will result largely in higher wages and salaries rather than lower prices.

Impact on United States trade

Growing money incomes in Europe will raise American exports. Even if the European economies grow no more rapidly than the 50 percent growth target set for the 1960's by the OECD, European imports from the rest of the world will rise by nearly $2 billion a year in the next few years and by around $3 billion a year by 1970. This compares with an annual increase in United States imports of $1.0-$1.5 billion if the United States maintains a similar rate of growth.[4] Higher growth rates in Europe would raise European imports still further. Not all of these imports would come from the United States, of course. Europe depends heavily for its growing industry on agricultural products and raw materials from all over the world. But the countries exporting primary products generally spend their export earnings as fast as they earn them; and, as in the past, a large part will be spent in the United States if American goods remain competitive. These crude figures, combined with our earlier conclusions about wage movements in Europe, suggest that

[4] These admittedly crude estimates result from applying marginal propensities to import from the rest of the world of .15 and .04 for Europe and the United States, respectively, to the annual increments in GNP resulting from a 4.1 percent growth rate. Increases in intra-European trade are excluded. Future propensities to import out of rising incomes will depend, of course, on relative price trends.

the United States trade balance, far from deteriorating, might improve substantially as a result of rapid economic growth in Europe.

The impact of this growth will not fall uniformly on all American exports. Growing amounts of raw materials will be required to feed Europe's expanding industry (although some of the most important technical improvements save on materials), but the United States has itself become a large net importer of many of these materials. Very likely Europe will displace the United States further in the production and fabrication of basic metals, a type of manufacturing in which economies of scale seem to be especially significant.

The future course of United States exports of foods and foodstuffs will depend more upon the common agricultural policy finally settled by the European Common Market than upon relative changes in productivity, although here is a field in which—thanks to the agricultural revolution which has taken place in the United States since the Second World War—Europe has more technological catching up to do than elsewhere.

Discussion earlier of the "demonstration effect" of high American living standards on Europeans suggests a sharp growth in demand for durable goods. Here Europe has a lot of catching up to do on the side of demand. While in the United States in 1959 there was one registered automobile for every three persons, in the Common Market countries there was only one automobile for every fourteen. Only 25 percent of all German households and 18 percent of all French households had refrigerators, compared with over 90 percent in the United States. Similar figures apply for washing machines and other appliances. Many European countries, moreover, are now just on the threshold of widespread use of consumer credit, a practice which should raise the demand for durables markedly—and, incidentally, will re-enforce worker preference for taking growing real income in the form of higher money wages rather than lower prices. No doubt the traditional American comparative advantage in the production of some consumer durables will slip away as European firms move into greater mass production of these items. But effective adaptation of American products to European needs would ensure for many years a growing market for American durables.

Finally, the very transformation of European industry from being geared to special orders and small production runs to being geared for large-scale mass production will raise European demand for just those types of goods—highly automated industrial equipment, electronic calculators and business machines, organic materials for synthetics—which the United States has pioneered in technical development. A higher degree of mechanization in both production and accounting require technical skills and specialized equipment in which the United States has substantial advantages in design, production, and installation.

Performance of the United States

The full impact of productivity growth in Europe on the United States obviously depends as much on the American response as on the European challenge. Any adjustments required in the United States will be eased by greater mobility and economic growth. Great importance should be attached to adequate programs for education to supply needed skills, to research and development expenditures to supply new products and techniques, and to a high rate of investment to assure that new products and techniques are rapidly diffused and new skills are used. With such programs the United States can remain the prime source for applied technology and can continue to improve its own productive efficiency.

As does Europe, the United States in principle faces a choice between taking its productivity increases in higher money incomes or in lower prices. In the past decade wage increases have *exceeded* improvements in productivity by a substantial margin. The economy cannot, over the long run, raise average money incomes faster than improvements in productivity without raising prices (or raising unemployment). While some excess of increases in income over increases in productivity is appropriate for a country with a chronic surplus in its balance of payments, it merely aggravates the problem of a country, such as the United States, with an external payments deficit. Hence the importance for the United States today of keeping increases in wages and other costs within—or even below—the bounds permitted by increases in productivity. In turn, the competitiveness of American products in world markets can be improved by translating cost-reducing increases in productivity into lower prices.

Conclusions

The unprecedented interest around the world in raising standards of living, and in adopting the techniques of production required to do so, will undoubtedly lead in time to a rise in productivity abroad relative to that in the United States. Even where advanced technology already enjoys wide application, economic growth and the formation of regional economic unions such as the European Common Market open the way to further improvements in productivity through increasing use of techniques of mass production and distribution. Expenditures in other countries for research and development will surely rise, and a European "know-how" in product innovation and production techniques may grow to rival the widely acclaimed American know-how.

With fixed exchange rates and low wages abroad, substantial increases in productivity open the possibility for a massive displacement of United States goods from world markets. Many fear that the United States will not be able to compete with the low unit labor costs apparently promised by low foreign wages and ever increasing productivity.

Two facts suggest taking a more measured view of rising productivity abroad, which after all permits higher standards of living throughout the world. First, the gap is likely to close far less rapidly than is sometimes imagined. At rates of increase in productivity plausible for the 1960's, it would take over 90 years for average European productivity to reach over-all productivity levels in the United States. Second, past increases in productivity have generally been taken in the form of higher incomes rather than lower prices. Rising productivity in Europe will not automatically lead to improved price competitiveness of European goods. Prospects for a tight labor market in most of Europe throughout the 1960's suggest that wage demands will keep up with, and perhaps (as in the past two years) even exceed advances in productivity.

To be sure, there will be problems of reallocation and adjustment brought about by rapid improvements in foreign productivity. In some product lines American firms will find it increasingly difficult to compete even in the United States market. But rising incomes abroad will raise foreign demands for other American products. The problem is not one of massive displacement of American goods from world markets, but of shifting American resources smoothly from industries with declining foreign demand to industries with rising foreign demand.

Francis Bello

9

The Technology Behind Productivity

When the American consumer became dissatisfied with the Model T, back in the Twenties, he made a decision of fateful importance for the United States economy. With this decision he proclaimed that he was more interested in the appearance and performance of a product than in its essential utility and basic cost. Had this decision not been made, Americans would today be spending less than $35 billion a year—ten percent of their total disposable income—on automobile transportation. Nor can the growing demand for compact cars be taken as evidence that the consumer now regrets his decision (or his father's decision) of 1925. The consumer has simply demanded, once again, a wider choice than Detroit has been willing to supply.

When United States manufacturers, and not just car makers, discovered that the American consumer regarded price as secondary, they naturally put primary emphasis on making their products as big, fast, shiny, convenient, and attractive as possible—laudable attributes, in many cases, but not cheap. The annual model change was born. At the same time manufacturers found it highly profitable to develop an endless succession of new products, and "optional extras," in which manufacturing cost and selling price are even less relevant than they are for old established products. Every car buyer knows, for example, that automatic transmissions, power brakes, power steering, and even two-toned finishes, are priced out of proportion to the price of the basic car. Thus it has come about that product improvement and product innovation absorb an overwhelming fraction of the billions of dollars that United States industry spends annually on research and development. The result has

Francis Bello *is on the board of editors of* Scientific American. *After starting his career as a chemist, Mr. Bello joined the staff of* Fortune *magazine, for which he was science editor from 1953 to 1960.*

been the spectacular and gadget-filled economy that is both our joy and our despair.

In only a few industries, notably those where the product is either immune to visible improvement or totally invisible (coal, gasoline, chemicals, electric power, telephone service), is major attention given to efficiency of production. (By any reasonable measure of value, the 2½ cent kilowatt hour and the 10 cent telephone call are the biggest bargains in the country.) For the most part, however, industry has hardly begun to apply to the manufacturing arts the technical ingenuity that has been applied to the development of consumer products and to the wonderful machines in power stations and telephone central offices that provide the most advanced consumer services. The ingenuity going into advanced military systems is perhaps two or three orders of magnitude beyond anything that can be found in the most highly automatic factory.

It is the thesis of this chapter, therefore, that United States industry has generally failed to put sufficient technical effort into raising the productivity of its mines, mills, factories, and offices. Far from pushing automation too fast, industry has not pushed it fast enough.

Because of this failure the nation may receive some unpleasant shocks before the decade is over. We may find that our productivity gains are barely holding at three percent a year, or even declining, while other nations are vigorously pushing theirs upward at rates of four, five, or even six percent—figures which have been maintained over the past decade in a number of western European countries, in Japan, and probably in the Soviet Union. All of these fast-growing countries still have large unfilled demands for goods and services, a relative shortage of labor, and therefore stronger incentives than the United States to achieve continued high gains in productivity. We must be prepared to see foreign governments—not just the Soviet Union—make the raising of productivity a major goal of domestic policy. If productivity keeps rising abroad while it stands still at home, we can look forward to a drastic decline in exports.

PRODUCTIVITY AT HOME AND ABROAD

Productivity rates, of course, are a very mixed bag, differing widely from one sector of the economy to another, and the rates in various sectors are not equally involved in the nation's ability to compete abroad. For export purposes it is more important that productivity keep rising strongly in agriculture, mining, manufacturing, transportation, utilities, and, to a lesser extent, in construction, which we may call collectively the "blue-collar" sectors, than in the "white-collar" sectors: wholesale and retail trade, finance, services, and government. These two broad divisions of the economy each account for almost exactly half of the Gross National Product and employ half of the labor force. Broadly speaking, the blue-collar group has shown somewhat higher productivity gains since 1947 than the white-collar group. The chief exceptions are construction and manufacturing, which have lagged slightly behind the economy as a whole. Since manufacturing is the largest single sector of the economy, employing slightly over 25 percent of all workers, its lag is significant. This chapter, unless otherwise noted, will be concerned primarily with productivity in the blue-collar sectors of the economy, which have the greatest bearing on the nation's ability to compete abroad.

Since it is not obvious that the total economy can grow fast enough to absorb blue-collar workers displaced by rising productivity, it may even be desirable that productivity *not* be accelerated in the white-collar sectors of the economy, which are least involved in keeping United States goods competitive in world markets. Although such deliberate manipulation of productivity rates may not appeal to classical economists, it could help reduce the social stresses in a decade that is bound to be stressful at best.

There is yet no evidence that the United States is ready to make the raising of productivity a national goal. To be sure, the annual report of the President's Council of Economic Advisers notes that the increase in productivity (gross national product per man-hour) fell from 3.4 percent a year in 1947 to 1954, to 2.4 percent a year in 1954 to 1960, and it suggests the need for a 3 percent annual rate in the Sixties. The report also offers some broad suggestions for achieving the 3 percent rate, but they are not very far-reaching, nor are they put forward with much sense of urgency.

It is easy to see, of course, why 3 percent is a comfortable rate. First, it is a rate we have achieved in the past and have found tolerable. Second, if the rate were any higher it would require a proportionately higher rate of total economic growth. The Council of Economic Advisers estimates that the man-hour input to the economy will grow at the rate of 1.5 percent a year between now and 1970 (compared to .6 percent a year from 1947 to 1960), so that the total economic growth rate, with a 3 percent annual rise in productivity, will add up to about 4.5 percent a year. If a greater productivity rise were desired for any reason—such as staying competitive in world markets—the GNP would have to grow proportionately faster to maintain employment, or else the work week would have to be proportionately shortened. Hence the dilemma that the United States may well have to face in the Sixties. There is nothing sacred about a 3 percent annual rise in productivity and if our world competitors should select, and achieve, a higher rate, we would have little choice but to try to keep up.

Under the circumstances it might be well to adopt the guiding principle, so often proved correct in weapons development and more recently in space technology, that if something is possible to do, it will be done—and probably sooner than most people expect. In productivity, and in the area commonly called automation, we may never see anything so dramatic as the Soviet Sputnik of October, 1957, but we should not be surprised if a country dedicated to raising its standard of living were to apply some of the same talents and imagination to raising productivity that it has applied to the exploration of space. Indeed, there is much evidence that the Soviet Union is taking automation very seriously—even to the extent of making up a Russian word to translate the term itself. There is now a Soviet Institute for Automation and Remote Control, with its own technical journal. There is also a Central Scientific Research Institute of Technology and Machinery and the Academy of Sciences, and the Ukrainian Republic has its own Institute of Machinery Construction and Automation.

The effectiveness of Soviet efforts to increase productivity, efforts far pre-dating the term *automation,* are now being officially recognized by Western economists. For example, analysts of the Rand Corporation estimate that the Soviet gross national product grew at a rate of 6 or 7 percent a year during the past decade, and that industrial output grew at the impressive rate of 9 percent. This compares with a United States growth rate, in the same period, of about 3.4 percent a year for the economy as a whole and about 3.8 percent a year in industrial output. Students of the Soviet economy believe that the Soviet Union will be able to maintain an industrial growth rate of at least 8 percent throughout the present decade. If the Soviet labor force is growing no faster than that in the United States—and, in fact, it is probably growing more slowly—the 8 percent industrial growth rate would translate into a productivity increase of about 6.5 percent a year. However, the over-all rate, including agriculture and services, may be only about two-thirds of that figure.

In the United States, in contrast to the Soviet Union, productivity is not formally the concern of any government agency. But it could be, and possibly it should be. It is only by custom and tradition that manufacturing processes are considered the most private domain of private industry. It was not so long ago that many companies refused to let outsiders into their plants, and even today, in the chemical and photographic industry, considerable secrecy remains. One of the great overworked phrases of World War II was "American know-how," meaning knowledge of how to produce things efficiently, knowledge so mysterious that it defied analysis.

Manufacturing efficiency has so many aspects that it indeed seems to defy analysis. The ability of men to improve at almost anything they attempt—whether it be piano playing, pole vaulting, or making things—is one of the deepest and most mysterious talents of the race. And there is almost no aspect of a society that does not have some bearing on its ability to produce goods and services. The members of the society must be healthy, educated, and provided with both suitable heroes and suitable tools. We will speak primarily of the tools, using the term in a broad sense.

One direct way to measure the effect of tools on productivity is to make a chart of investment in plant and equipment (business capital stock) per worker and compare it with change in output per worker. The President's Council of Economic Advisers have published such a study; the figures represent changes in percent per year:

	1929 to 1947	1947 to 1954	1954 to 1960	1947 to 1960
Capital stock per worker	0.0	3.5	1.9	2.7
Output per worker	1.5	3.3	2.1	2.8

This shows, first, that although the value of the tools available to workers did not increase over the entire period, 1929-1947, the output of the worker climbed 1.5 percent a year anyway. Presumably any new tools provided to replace old tools in this period were better than the tools they replaced. Moreover, 1929-1947 marked the hey-day of the efficiency expert and the time-and-motion study engineer. With little money to invest in machinery during the Depression, business managers concentrated on getting more production out of existing machines. Presumably, too, the Depression permitted management to select the most efficient workers from the labor pool. Postwar, the table shows, output per worker moved almost exactly in step with investment per worker. It also appears that in the most recent 6-year period, 1954 to 1960, output rose faster than investment, which implies that the tools of this period were more efficient, dollar-for-dollar, than the tools of the prior 7-year period.

What one would like to be able to measure, of course, is the effect of investment on research and development on output per worker over the long run. Economists have found the topic a baffling one, and the Council of Economic Advisers (1962 report) confines itself to a modest statement: "The limited data available suggest that within industries and between industries there is a positive correlation between research effort and productivity growth."

The problem is to distinguish between research that advances knowledge relevant to production and research that does not, whatever other benefits it may bring. The fact is that the great bulk of research performed in the United States today is so conceived and directed that its effect on productivity is relatively slight. Except for a limited amount of basic research, almost all research and development sponsored by the government, which supplies about 60 percent of all research funds, is product oriented. The products are primarily the familiar ones: weapons systems, military electronics, and space vehicles.

The main business of the civilian part of the economy is providing goods and services for private consumers. Last year they spent about $42 billion for durable goods, $156 billion for non-durables, $141 billion for services, and $21 billion for new homes—a total of $360 billion. By comparison, in 1961, only about $39 billion was invested in new plant and equipment by all United States industry and agriculture combined.

Business, consequently, can justify much more research on consumer products and services than on machines for farms, mines and factories. DuPont can afford to spend $20 million developing orlon and $50 million developing its latest polymer, Delrin. RCA spent $55 million on black and white television and another $130 million on color television before they became profitable. The automobile industry put tens of millions into development of automatic transmissions.

Because the private consumer is the hero of the United States economic system, the big companies get short shrift when they assume the role of consumer. When General Motors or General Electric wants a new factory, it cannot find a G.M. or G.E. to build it. A factory is not a product. It is a painstakingly assembled collection of machines drawn from many sources, conceived for many purposes, with technical ancestries dating back 20, 50 or 100 years. When they are brought under one roof they must be forcibly integrated to do the job at hand. The whole concept of "system," raised to such high sophistication in the design of weapons, and still earlier in the engineering of the vast Bell telephone network, is missing. The systems concept requires precise specification of a goal, thoughtful optimization of the engineering variables, followed by development of all components to do the job required without excess size, cost or complexity. To design and engineer an automobile factory under this rigorous concept is probably beyond the resources of any single firm.

Within the last 15 years Detroit has made a small start in this direction by fostering development of "transfer machines," which actually inspired the term automation. These are specially designed metalworking machines arranged in a series and tied together by a conveyor system that accurately positions the work piece as it is carried from station to station. At the Ford engine plant in Cleveland, rough castings of engine blocks are transferred into and out of 20-odd machines that perform more than 500 separate operations of broaching, milling, boring, honing, drilling and tapping.

Plants of this sort are still primitive, however, compared to a modern refinery or chemical plant. The oil and chemical firms have spent more technical effort on the manufacturing process than the firms in any other industry. Actually, they had no choice. In these industries one does not have a product until one has developed a process for making it. The continuous-flow refinery and chemical plant are new creations in this century. The precise control of gases and fluids in huge volumes, at high velocities and temperatures, required development of a new art of materials handling, and the oil and chemical firms had to create it almost single handed. The principal "machine tools" of the refinery and chemical plant are the fractionating towers, which accurately separate desired from undesired compounds, and the catalytic reactors that convert compounds of low value into compounds of higher value. Unhampered by tradition, the oil and chemical firms have added continuously to the capacity, flexibility and precision of these tools.

Along the way, these firms conceived a new and brilliant development technique, the "pilot plant." This is a miniature manufacturing unit having an output of roughly 100 to 1000 times that possible in laboratory equipment, but only one-hundredth or one-thousandth that of a full-size plant. Its purpose is to provide the engineering data and experience from which a commercial plant can be designed. Typical pilot plants may cost from a few hundred thousand dollars to a million or more, but they return their cost many times over. It is not surprising that refineries and chemical plants designed in this way have an integrity and an efficiency far beyond what has been achieved in the factories that produce our automobiles, stoves, refrigerators, dishwashers, television sets and other consumer durables.

WHAT KIND OF RESEARCH RAISES PRODUCTIVITY?

Let me now try to identify in the nation's research and development budget the expenditures having the most direct bearing on productivity. Having done that, I will make some observations about the size and adequacy of these expenditures. For this examination one can draw on the National Science Foundation report, "Funds for Research and Development in Industry, 1959," the last full survey available at this writing. These surveys, sponsored by the NSF and conducted by the Bureau of the Census, date back only to 1953, but in this period they have become one of the most useful and fascinating documents published by the government.

In trying to identify expenditures that bear on productivity, one must recognize the complex nature of the industrial economy. A product like nylon has little or no influence on productivity in the hosiery industry, where it is simply a replacement for silk. But when nylon is molded and used to replace a mechanical gear in a car or washing machine, it can reduce labor input and thus raise productivity. In short, new technological products, even those inspired by consumer needs, will often lead to simplifications and cost reduction in manufacturing processes.

There are other consequences of research still harder to identify and measure. The jet transport began as a military product and ultimately became a civilian product. The ability it provides to cross the country in 5 hours instead of 8 must have many indirect effects on the economy and on the productivity of highly-paid executives. Or, to take another example in the area of communications, what has been the economic effect of the increase in telephone conversations from 140 million a day in 1950 to 219 million a day in 1960—a growth of 56 percent? And what is it worth to American business to save a few seconds on every long distance call, thanks to direct long distance dialing?

Leaving aside such intangibles, let us examine the nation's research outlay in 1959. That year industrial laboratories performed research and development valued at $9.5 billion, of which private companies supplied $3.9 billion and the federal government $5.6 billion. Five industrial categories accounted for 85 percent of the total expenditures: aircraft and parts ($3,030 million), electrical equipment and communication ($2,240 million), chemicals ($950 million), machinery ($950 million), and motor vehicles ($870 million).

Of all the industrial groups listed (14 categories in all), the machinery industry is the one whose products are tied most broadly and intimately to productivity. This industry provides machinery in great variety not just for the blue-collar sectors of the economy but also for the nation's business and government offices. The products of the machinery industry include: engines and turbines; farm equipment; construction, mining and materials-handling machinery; metalworking machinery; machines for the food, textile, paper, printing, and wood-working industries; general industrial machines (such as pumps, compressors, ovens); and—finally—business machines, computers and electronic data processing equipment.

Now although firms *classified* in the machinery industry spent $950 million on R&D in 1959, some of this money was spent on things other than machines. And, by the same token, laboratories in other industries did a certain amount of development on machines of various kinds. For example, a company like General Electric, which is classified in the electrical equipment industry, develops and builds both turbines and computers, which are classified as machines.

Fortunately, the NSF report provides a breakdown, cutting across industry lines, to show how much R&D money actually went into machinery, and it turns out not to be $950 million but only $765 million. It also turns out that almost 40 percent of this sum ($290 million) went into development of office machinery and computers. The next largest single figure was $154 million for engines and turbines. Farm machinery received $66 million, and $54 million was spread across construction, mining, and materials-handling machinery. Metalworking machinery, classically regarded as the machines that make machines, received only $42 million. And all other machinery accounted for $158 million.

Nearly half (48 percent) of the total figure of $765 million was provided by the federal government, which means that private industry, in 1959, spent only $370 million doing research and development on the tools and machines having the most direct effect on productivity. This figure, about a million dollars a day, is one we wish to keep in mind.

Now, what other R&D expenditures have a close effect on productivity? One important category is that covering scientific and mechanical measuring instruments, which includes all the remarkable process control instruments so important to the high efficiency of the oil and chemical industries. In 1959 the combined federal and private R&D expenditures on such devices was about $155 million, of which industry's share was something under $60 million.

There is, finally, one other type of technological effort having an important bearing on productivity, and that is research and development on new and improved manufacturing processes. Although the NSF has tried to determine how R&D funds are divided between products and processes, it has had difficulty obtaining figures that it considers good enough to publish. Perhaps the only figures throwing significant light on this question are those reported in 1958 by McGraw-Hill. Industrial laboratories were asked to state how R&D funds were divided among "new products," "improved products," and "new processes," with the following results (the dollar investment in "new processes" for 1959 has been obtained by applying the indicated percentages to the NSF data on total 1959 expenditures by each industry).

Industry	New Products	Improved Products	New Processes	Est. 1959 R&D on New Processes ($ in millions)
Electric machinery	68%	32%	0%	—
Other machinery	51	46	3	16
Transp. equip.	56	39	5	—
Chemicals & drugs	67	27	6	40
Motor vehicles	50	42	8	50
Stone, glass, clay	42	48	10	7
Paper & pulp	37	50	13	8
Textiles	37	47	16	—
Rubber	50	33	17	12
Food	53	28	19	16
Iron & steel	27	46	27	20
Non-ferrous metals	64	9	27	14
Petroleum	29	29	42	100
Industry average	48	41	11	—

The events of April, 1962, when the steel industry raised prices $6 a ton and then quickly rescinded them in the face of White House pressure, point up the significance of the figures in this table. The steel industry claimed that unless it had the price increase it could not keep modernizing its plants to meet foreign competition and the domestic competition of other products, such as aluminum and plastics. The fact is that the industry, in the decade 1951-1960, had already spent an enormous sum— over $11 billion, replacing worn-out equipment and adding almost exactly 50 percent to its ingot capacity. But because these modernizations did not reflect a very significant advance in technology, they raised the steel industry's productivity per man-hour only about 2 percent a year. To account for this low productivity rise one only has to look at the industry's tiny expenditure on process research and development. As nearly as can be estimated, the industry spent less than $150 million on this activity in the decade 1951-1960. This works out to less than 15 cents per ton of steel poured in this period, and represents less than 1.5 cents for every $1 of new plant investment. For lack of adequate research and development the industry has paid dearly—perhaps too dearly—for its modest productivity gains. It is sometimes overlooked that an important goal of process development is to lower the cost of the new processes that research has discovered, thereby reducing the cost of new plant investment. Having neglected process research and development in the Fifties, the steel industry enters the Sixties ill-equipped to raise productivity any faster in the new decade than in the last one.

The sharply contrasting figures for the oil industry can be quickly stated. Its investment in new refineries and petro-chemical plants, 1951-1960, came to about $7.7 billion and its investment in process research to about $850 million. How the planned funds and research funds were allocated between refineries and chemical plants unfortunately is not known. The process research figure represents an investment of over 10 cents for every $1 of new plant investment. The payoff can be found in refinery productivity, which rose at the rate of about 5 percent a year during the decade.

Actually, the oil industry, as the table shows, provided about one-fourth of the total industry expenditure on process research. The total expenditure in 1959 came to about $420 million, obtained by applying 11 percent to the $3.8 billion of company funds invested in applied R&D that year.

We are now ready to attempt a summing up. We reckoned previously that private R&D investment in machinery was $370 million in 1959, and that the investment in scientific and control instruments was another $60 million, for a total of $430 million. Ignoring some slight overlapping among the various figures, we can add this $430 million to the $420 million spent on new processes, for a total of $850 million—or, to use a round number, $.9 billion. To this must be added the federal contribution of almost $400 million for development work on machinery and another $100 million for work on instruments.[1] This gives a grand

---

[1] Undoubtedly a certain amount (much less than 11 percent) of the government's $5.6 billion R&D expenditure in 1959 contributed to work on new processes, but it did not seem that an unsupported estimate would be of any value to this discussion.

total of some $1.4 billion as the 1959 national investment in new technology directly applicable to productivity.

Now $1.4 billion is not an inconsiderable sum. Nor is $.9 billion. But is either enough?

The private investment figure is only $5 a person, or less than 0.2 percent of the GNP. It is substantially less than the $1.4 billion spent on television advertising in 1959, and less than 10 percent of the total sum ($11 billion) spent on advertising in all forms. All of us are aware, because we have been told so often, that advertising is the most powerful force in the economy. It creates the demand that builds the plants that employs the workers, etc. But one may still be astonished that American business finds it profitable to spend $11 on advertising for every 90 cents spent on research to raise productivity. It seems clear that if we are in world competition with countries that choose to place a different and higher value on raising productivity, we will not stay in the race very long.

A PROPOSAL FOR RAISING PRODUCTIVITY

Let us try to imagine, therefore, what might happen if the United States government were to decide that a 3 percent a year rise in productivity is not good enough. Although impossible to demonstrate, short of actually trying, we could probably achieve by 1975 or 1980 an average productivity growth of 5 or 6 percent a year in the blue-collar half of the economy (agriculture, mining, manufacturing, transportation, utilities, and construction) where productivity has been growing recently at about 4 percent a year. This higher growth rate could almost certainly be achieved at less cost in research and development than it will take to get to the moon. The space budget, which was $178 million in the year of Sputnik, grew exactly 10 times by the fiscal year of 1961. In fiscal 1962 it will be $3.1 billion, and the request for fiscal 1963 is $5.5 billion. The figure is expected to reach $7 billion a year and then level out for the rest of the Sixties.

Perhaps half this sum, specifically devoted to research on productivity, would be enough to raise the going rate in the blue-collar sectors of the economy to 5 or 6 percent a year—but not by 1970. In this sense, it is harder to raise productivity than to reach the moon. The factories that will be built over the next half dozen years will have to depend largely on technology already in hand, or well advanced, today. The productivity of 1970 will be quite firmly frozen by 1965, at the latest. But a determined assault on the productivity problem could begin to yield significant results, clearly visible in the national economic statistics, by 1975.

The task of raising productivity is inherently so difficult that one can say with some confidence that it will *not* be significantly raised as a simple by-product of the space expenditure. To gain support for the huge space budgets, Congress and the country is being told that the lunar voyage, promised before 1970, will provide rich dividends for the civilian economy. This theme first emerged in the President's State of the Union Message, in January, 1962. "Our aim," President Kennedy said, "is not simply to be the first on the moon, any more than Charles Lindbergh's real aim was to be first in Paris. His aim was to develop the techniques and the authority of this country . . . in the field of the air and the atmosphere. And our objective in making this effort, which we hope will place one of our citizens on the moon, is to develop in a new frontier of science, commerce and cooperation, the position of the United States and the free world."

The same point was made rather more explicitly in the President's 1962 report to the Congress on United States aeronautics and space activities. The report states: "In the national interest, the United States must build the capacity to advance the most modern science and technology to the utmost, and extract from it the wealth of benefits it holds for this country's freedom, economy, professions, education, and standard of living."

This is a delusive theme if "standard of living" is properly translated to mean "productivity." The space program will add immensely to our knowledge of the universe. Weather satellites will increase the accuracy of weather forecasting and possibly lead to weather control. Communication satellites will relay telephone messages and television programs to every point on the globe. In short, the space program will richly exploit the uses of space. It will probably yield some exotic new materials, new products, and new services, as well. But it will not, in all likelihood, simplify or reduce the cost of mining coal, smelting ore, extracting oil, building houses, or assembling automobiles. It will not lower the cost of putting food on the table, clothes on our backs, or shoes on our feet.

Not is a strong word. Anything *might* come out of the space program, just as anything might come out of the atomic energy program. In designing automobiles, General Motors might discover a new drug. In designing drugs, Merck might discover a new fuel for automobiles. But it is not reasonable to base public policy on the improbable.

What we have learned from half a century of conducting industrial research on a steadily larger and more sophisticated scale is that technology can be programmed, that carefully defined goals can be reached —once fundamental knowledge is in hand. Before the discovery of nuclear fission, it would have been futile to try to build an atomic power plant. After fission was discovered, and it was shown that nature permitted a nuclear chain reaction, the road to atomic power lay wide open.

The road to higher productivity in virtually every industry is similarly open today. The road can always be shortened, of course, by new fundamental discoveries, which is why we must continue to nurture basic research. But for most technological purposes it is usually found that what is lacking is not basic knowledge, but the skill and ingenuity to use effectively what is already known. This is true of the space program itself. There is no fundamental reason why a satellite could not have been put into orbit the same year that Lindbergh flew to Paris, or even earlier. Satellites were not being built in 1927 for essentially the same reason—no easier to understand—that no one was running a four-minute mile in that year.

How the Job Might Be Done

The problem of raising productivity has two aspects: finding another $2 billion or so a year to add to the R&D sums now being spent for machines, control instruments, and new processes, and, perhaps more difficult, creating a program that will approach in excitement the space, atomic energy and other technical programs competing for the available scientific and engineering talent. Providing the money is chiefly a political task. Some of it can be raised, though probably much less than half, by offering private industry tax and other incentives. Probably the bulk of $2 billion will have to be provided directly by the government. At this late date, there should be no skittishness about government intervention on this scale. We already have government investment to thank for jet transports, atomic power plants, and electronic computers. Raising productivity is obviously another task too big to be left solely to private enterprise.

Careful thought must be given to the design of the program. Is this to be a job for the Department of Commerce, or do we need another agency on the level of the AEC or NASA? How much of the R&D money should be spent within industry and how much should be channeled into newly-created government laboratories? Such laboratories could be modeled after the AEC's system of National Laboratories (Los Alamos, Brookhaven, Oak Ridge, Argonne, Livermore). Other models are the Jet Propulsion Laboratory operated for NASA by the California Institute of Technology and the Lincoln Laboratory operated for the Air Force by the Massachusetts Institute of Technology. There would be obvious advantages to having productivity laboratories tied closely to the great engineering schools. There should also be deliberate regional coverage through association with leading schools in the Midwest and South, as well as East and West. The recent decision to let the AEC's Oak Ridge Laboratory work on water desalting suggests that Oak Ridge and other AEC laboratories could be assigned a substantial role in raising productivity.

In addition to such working laboratories there is a clear need for a long-range thinking and planning organization comparable to the Rand Corporation, which would carry out comprehensive economic and social studies on productivity. Part of its job would be to identify sectors of industry where productivity is moving sluggishly, to make projections of the impact of productivity changes on labor requirements, and to devise retraining programs. No single counterpart of Rand could examine all the social and economic consequences of an energetic program to raise productivity. The government would also have to draw heavily on the social science departments of our major universities for advice and guidance.

There are two general reasons for believing that productivity can be accelerated at an unprecedented rate in the decades ahead. The first is the evidence presented here that industry, by and large, has never really put its back into the job. The second, and more compelling reason, is that technological advances in electronics and data processing now make it possible, in principle, to build machines that will carry out virtually any manufacturing operation performed by men.

Having said this, however, one must add immediately that it is almost never practical or profitable to design a machine that will simply duplicate the sensory abilities, hand movements, and logical processes that a man uses in doing a particular job. If automation consisted only in this, the job of building automatic factories would be a straightforward problem of designing electronically-controlled man-like machines. But to do the job efficiently, which means at an acceptable cost, the whole manufacturing (or mining, or farming, or transportation, or construction) process must be rethought in terms of the special characteristics of the machine. This, of course, has been said many times and, like most generalizations, it is not very enlightening. The point is that the automobile is not pulled by an engine with four mechanical legs and the airplane is not thrust through the air by flapping wings.

There are other reasons for not copying biological systems slavishly. For example, about a dozen years ago the thought occurred to a number of engineers that it should be possible to replace a machine-tool operator by a set of instructions encoded on paper tape or magnetic tape. One attractive idea was simply to tape record the tool settings employed by a highly-skilled machinist. It turned out that even the best machinists are rather less skillful than had been thought, and, worse yet, are more inclined to get flustered than a concert artist during a taping session.

This approach was therefore abandoned in favor of working out mathematically a full program of instructions that could subsequently be transferred to tape.

When industry is ready to design an automatic factory it can draw on a variety of highly sophisticated mathematical concepts. Servomechanism theory, which embraces the principles of control and guidance used in missiles, can provide the means for making products to high tolerance with a minimum of scrap. By extension the theory can also provide manufacturing flexibility. The theory of error-correcting codes will make it possible for electronic control devices, and for computers tied into production processes, to operate continuously for months on end with an infinitesimal error rate. A variation of this concept has already led to the design of reliable electronic circuits built from unreliable components. As this development is extended, one can visualize elaborate manufacturing systems that rarely need maintenance. An alternative possibility is to build systems that are self-repairing. What distinguishes the present epoch from all previous ones is that large cadres of young scientists and engineers have been trained to think along such lines. Until now their thinking has been directed almost exclusively to the design of exotic military and space systems, but it could be channeled into thinking about manufacturing systems, a task that would be every bit as challenging.

*   *   *   *   *   *

The arguments put forward in this chapter can be quickly summarized. Able students of the economy believe that United States economic growth should be at the rate of about 4.5 percent a year to enable the nation to fulfill its domestic and foreign obligations. To achieve this growth rate in the Sixties will require a growth in output per man-hour of 3 percent a year. The recent past performance of the economy indicates that this growth in productivity may be difficult to achieve. Examination of the nation's research and development expenditures shows that only about 15 percent, or $1.4 billion, of the total 1959 budget of $9.5 billion could be identified as bearing directly on productivity. Since business evidently lacks the incentive to raise this figure significantly, it should be made a matter of national concern and raised by government decision to around $3.5 billion a year, or to about 30 percent of the prevailing R&D budget. It seems reasonable to estimate that this would provide, by 1975 or 1980, a productivity growth rate of 5 or 6 percent a year in the half of the economy made up of agriculture, mining, manufacturing, transportation, utilities, and construction.

To me the choice seems clear. It is better to aim for such a growth rate aggressively, in full awareness of the social consequences, and with federal agencies equipped to deal with the resulting problems, than to drift along as at present, fearful that the growth rate will be too low, and poorly equipped to handle the social problems that even a low rate produces. If it is desirable that men have wealth without working—which remains to be proved, of course—there can never be too much automation.

Henry M. Wriston

10

Perspective

Automation involves so sharp an acceleration of technological change as virtually to inaugurate a new epoch. Without wise and vigorous foresight and action, it can have violently disruptive effects—consequences which could be comparable, in their fundamental dislocations, to the impact of rapid industrialization upon underdeveloped areas of the world.

These considerations make both discussion and action urgent. In the desire to arouse the public to these important issues, however, there is a tendency to underestimate the time available and to overstate the speed of change. The first digital computers are already a generation old; the volume on Cybernetics was published well over a decade ago. The state of the art of automation is highly fluid; many instruments are obsolescent when installed, and obsolete in 5 years or less. The design, construction, installation, and programming for any sizable plant take some years. The speed of adopting automation as a way of production will not be uniform, nor will its level of sophistication be high in most corporations for many years to come. While there is no time to waste, there is enough time to absorb the shocks if preparation is pursued with energy and wisdom.

During the Industrial Revolution of the 18th and 19th centuries, society had neither the economic, psychological, or sociological knowledge, nor the political know-how to cope with the hardships occasioned by mechanization and the factory system. The result was a long period of exceedingly harsh social, economic, and political readjustment. We cannot afford, nor do we need, to accept a repetition of such strains. In a modern democracy they would prove socially, economically, and politically intolerable.

During the last half century society's capacity to absorb revolutionary

HENRY M. WRISTON *is President of The American Assembly.*

changes has greatly increased. Research and experience in many fields have given us new intellectual tools; they can be improved still more. Government and industry have learned to cooperate flexibly; their partnership must be more fully implemented. The range and ingenuity of our social agencies have vastly increased, and must continue to grow. Education, with all its deficiencies, has already made our population infinitely more adaptable to changes of many kinds, including the industrial. It has a yet greater role in the years ahead.

Despite the closing of the frontier and the sensational growth of home ownership, the mobility of the work force has not been seriously impaired; the pessimistic predictions of the past have been largely forgotten. Every year millions of workers voluntarily join and leave the labor force; other millions change jobs and move from one place to another. About 7 per cent of all male workers live in a county different from the one they inhabited last year; more than half of those who moved live in a different state. This development is just another indication of man's remarkable adaptability; there is no reason why it should not continue, especially if his educational level rises.

For workers and managers automation brings altered roles with attendant psychological pressures; from individuals it demands new habits and tastes. Automation requires changes in orientation for entire communities—a transformation of the content of our culture. These effects can be as demanding as the benefits can be salutary.

Initial impacts

In attempting to make even the most tentative assessments of the psychological and sociological impact of automation, however, there is a grave danger lest we do what has been done so often before—look at the matter in short perspective and make sweeping generalizations upon the basis of inadequate experience. It has been demonstrated time and time again that the generation upon whom the first impact falls has one reaction, but the next generation shows no like reaction. In short, the capacity to absorb change is progressive as novelty wears off. The word *sabotage* derives from the throwing of wooden shoes into power looms during the early years of the Industrial Revolution. Featherbedding was and continues to be the reaction of a later generation to yet another change. In thinking about the impact of automation, therefore, we should take a much longer perspective and, without neglecting the severe adjustments that must be made by the current generation, think much more about the effects of automation when those adjustments will have been almost forgotten.

The copyists had a psychological shock when the typewriter came in, but it is only with the effort of historical imagination that we can even begin to understand how they felt. In 1920, I was told by one of the oldest State Department employees that when the first typewriter salesman approached the department—traditionally the most conservative of all in Washington—he was rejected on the ground that the copyists were swift enough. He was thrown out on successive attempts until he finally came in with a proposition which seemed to the chief of the section so preposterous that he could not refuse it. The demonstrator offered to write the words *Washington Monument* on the typewriter as rapidly as the scrivener could write one short word. When he successfully proved that he could do that, the official reluctantly admitted that typewriters were probably here to stay. As always in change, the initial impact was severe, but even the memory of that drastic change-over is all but lost.

With automation, as with the typewriter, the benefits are sufficient to justify strenuous efforts. New stress must be placed upon cost savings and price reductions in which the public has not adequately shared in recent years. Greater variety and better quality of goods can be produced; the consumer should have a broader range for discriminating choice. There must be much wider distribution both at home and abroad. Attention should be given to even greater mobility of labor. Industry must accelerate the elimination of drudgery and other tendencies to boredom. Energy should go into the creation of new and better jobs, in distribution and in services, as well as in production. The exploitation of leisure for citizenship and for personal fulfillment must be vastly more effective.

Leisure

Through most of history, back-breaking manual labor for long hours has been the lot of both men and women, leaving little time or energy for cultural activity. That is still the rule in most of the world. Making a virtue of necessity being a fundamental human trait, a system of ethics based upon the virtues of labor was elaborated. The roots of such a philosophy appear even as early as the third chapter of Genesis: "In the sweat of thy face shalt thou eat bread." As this tradition matured, there was a strong tendency to equate leisure with idleness and idleness with sin. The idea of educating the masses for leisure was not even suggested.

At the other end of the scale a small class of men was free of the physical burdens of manual labor. Thus there arose a great aristocratic tradition in the arts. This was reflected in classic form in Ecclesiasticus: "The wisdom of the Scribe cometh by opportunity of leisure; and he that hath little business shall become wise." His privileged status as a learned man was there contrasted with that of the laborer: "How shall he become wise that holdeth the plow, that glorieth in the shaft of the goad, that driveth

oxen. . . . He will set his heart upon turning his furrows; and his wake-
fulness is to give his heifers their fodder. . . . So is every artificer and
workmaster."

Automation will accelerate the development of a new leisure class.
Far from being an aristocratic élite, it will be democratic in composition
and temper. The reduction in hours of work and in physical arduousness
has already proceeded more rapidly than the maturation of a constructive
philosophy of leisure for the working man. Increased longevity has accen-
tuated the effects of that deficiency. With increasing time to himself, man
is more than ever in need of improved taste, more diversified interests,
more constructive social values, a more active sense of citizenship, and
higher individual ideals. It is essential to develop a theory of leisure as
the basis for genuine personal enrichment. The attainment of that goal
will call for self-discipline at least as rigorous as has been demanded by
arduous labor in the past.

Current appraisals of the wasteful and trivial—not to say demoralizing
—uses to which the new leisure has so far been put are probably accurate.
In this field, as in others, however, too much prediction about the future
is based upon straight-line extrapolations of current deficiencies. This
makes the outlook exceedingly pessimistic. But the habits of a mature
generation formed under one set of experiences should not be projected
as valid for a younger generation differently educated and living in an
altered environment. We have no measure of human potentialities for
the use of leisure because they have never before had adequate consideration in mass education. The time has come for broader and deeper culti-
vation of the arts, sciences, and humanities at every level. Imaginatively
taught, they can help toward understanding urgent public questions and
give a meaningful direction to the use of leisure.

Education and training

For almost a century, since the passage of the Morrill Act, too much
emphasis has been placed on narrow vocational training. There is need
for reform in this area; tremendous stress must be laid upon principles
rather than techniques. Mere procedures increasingly become obsolete
before they can be taught, much less applied. Education should aim for
the development of flexibility to help people shift from one form of work
to another when necessary as more broadly educated men and women are
accustomed to do. A brief perusal of careers recorded in *Who's Who in
America* shows the enormous range and the frequency of such changes
of occupation among the highly educated. Similar flexibility of employment must be extended to those in lines of work which are seldom reflected
in *Who's Who*.

Fresh approaches to management training are also important if automation is to be widely practicable. Static concepts of management are as surely doomed as traditional occupations at the level of the mechanic or the clerk. Advance toward more effective use of automation is still retarded by the persistence in many policy-making circles of out-dated ideas regarding management. Statesmanlike management has a great opportunity for a more constructive approach. It must show imagination in order to capitalize on the positive opportunities for large-scale achievement.

In the short run there is the severe problem of training in new skills for workers whose present skills are no longer needed. The fact that automation cannot be instantly used in all plants in any industry, however, means that there will still be employment opportunities for the older or otherwise less adaptable workers. They can continue to find work in plants not yet automated if our employment services are strengthened.

The need for common labor has been steadily declining throughout this century; it will surely shrink rapidly in the future. What to do with people lacking capacity for anything beyond elementary education has been a growing problem. This issue needs intensive research lest we develop an element entirely alien to the new way of life.

Role of government

Taking advantage of automation's long-run benefits, as well as meeting transient, albeit serious, problems, such as local unemployment, will call for wise judgment and administration both public and private. The simple and obvious course is to turn to the federal government. Secretary of Labor Goldberg has created a new group in the Department to make a special study of automation problems. A negative approach could well lead to restrictive legislation in order to slow the pace of change. To follow such a course is to postpone benefits far greater than the losses involved in the rapid spread of new processes.

Too great a reliance upon government can bog down progress in bureaucratic complexity and compromise. The sensational technical and scientific advances in agriculture have created a surplus of 1.5 million farm laborers. But extemporized government measures have in many instances actually retarded necessary and inevitable adjustments, such as retiring uneconomic farms and the resettlement, retraining, and re-employment of surplus farmers. Such temporizing with great social problems cannot be tolerated as automation accelerates.

International aspects

The international implications of automation are no less than colossal. The dramatic shrinkage of the world and the more intimate interdependence of nations will be sharply advanced. For the United States is not alone in its resort to automation. We are among the earliest and most vigorous in its employment. Its more intensive use is essential to effective competition with economies having excessively cheap manpower.

Automation is so explosive a force that it would disrupt any closed economic system, even in a nation as large, as varied, and as rich as ours. It marks the end of any rational resort to isolation and protectionism. For better or for worse we are in the midst of a world-stream and must navigate it with boldness as well as skill. Ultimately only open societies, transcending national lines, can adequately exploit automation and bring its benefits to the citizens of the world.

American society and the world economy are neither of them inert. Our own potential ingenuity in meeting the new demands is unpredictably great. We need to remember, moreover, that the need for goods is not limited to present high consumption groups in the United States, or even in the advanced nations. Automation is indispensable in expanding production at low cost to meet the demands of the millions in underdeveloped nations for goods which they cannot now produce, and are unlikely to be able to provide in the foreseeable future. With intelligent and vigorous application, automation can help in the immensely difficult task of raising the standard of living among the desperately poor of the world.

Final Report of the Twenty-first American Assembly

At the close of their discussions the participants in the Twenty-first American Assembly at Arden House, Harriman, New York, May 3-6, 1962, on AUTOMATION AND TECHNOLOGICAL CHANGE, reviewed as a group the following statement. Although there was general agreement on the Final Report, it is not the practice of The American Assembly for participants to affix their signatures, and it should not be assumed that every participant necessarily subscribes to every recommendation.

THE CHALLENGE AND THE PROMISE OF TECHNOLOGY

The objectives of the American people call for acceleration of the pace of technological progress.

Greater productivity is essential for higher living standards, increased leisure, and jobs for the growing population. It is vital to our competitive position and to the economic strength of the free world in competition with communist nations.

Education is both the root of technological change and the basis for successful adaptation. We must become a more versatile people, with more skills and broader understanding of the modern world. A new national attitude, in which education is universally prized and innovation universally welcomed, is the key to the progress of the American people in the age of automation.

Technological change has already brought or has made possible vast benefits in the form of higher living standards, new products, better control over disease, less back-breaking toil and the opportunities created by more leisure. But it has also involved new challenges ranging from the terror of modern warfare to dislocations in skills and employment, and in local communities. Moreover, these disruptions have caused increasing concern as the American people have become more sensitive to the human costs involved. A free society should not ignore the sometimes devastating effect of change upon individuals.

Today, technological change involves elements not found in the early days of the industrial revolution. There is now an increasing scientific base for technology; the steam engine antedated thermodynamics, but the applications of atomic energy were developed from a discovery in physics. A new industry of discovery has been created in recent years. Large private and public resources are devoted to research and development. Annual expenditures for science and technology have grown from $500 million in 1940 to over $12 billion today. The federal government is playing a new role in research. Technological change now affects office, white-collar and management jobs. The net effect of these developments is that technological change is now so rapid that revolutionary consequences may well emerge in the course of this decade.

While the word *automation* properly refers to automatic control of continuous processes, automatic transfer equipment, and computers for data processing and controls, the larger process of technological change and its impacts are the concern of this American Assembly.

Technological change involves a complex social process including many elements: science, education, research and development under private and public auspices, management, technology, production facilities, workers and labor organizations. Increases in productivity and broadening the industrial base are among the results of this process. In order to raise the rate of increase, the performance of this process at all stages must be improved. All groups in the community have a contribution to make. No single body determines the rate of increase and no law can raise it by simple decree. To accelerate productivity is a challenge to our technical resourcefulness, our capacity to cooperate, our political ingenuity and our sense of national purpose.

The direction and rate of technological change in our society have been responsive to competitive pressures and market opportunities, to the priorities of public policy as reflected in appropriations for medical research, atomic energy, defense and space, and to scientific advances. Public policy may play an even larger role in these matters.

A wide variety of policies—short-run and long-run—is required to improve significantly the results of the complex process of technological change. Some are private, some public; others require new forms of cooperation between government and private groups.

RECOMMENDATIONS FOR PRIVATE AND PUBLIC POLICIES

I. *A High-Employment Economy*—A high level of effective demand is the first requisite to the rapid adjustments involved in a technologically advanced and dynamic economy. The availability of more and better jobs gives workers incentives for high performance at present skills and the learning of new skills; it facilitates occupational and geographical transfers when these are necessary. It also gives young people the incentive to apply themselves adequately to education and training. The difficulty of readjustments associated with technological change is greatly increased when unemployment is widespread and of long duration.

We should not underestimate the capacity of the American economy to create jobs; the number of jobs was increased from 52.8 to 66.8 million in the period 1945-61. However, recent levels of unemployment have been unsatisfactory and the next decade will witness vast additions to the labor force. The maintenance of a high level of employment is a basic goal.

II. *A Versatile and Educated Work Force*—A major problem associated with current technological change is the imbalance between the type of labor force our new technology increasingly requires and the skills and qualifications of the present labor force and of the new entrants. Far too many have inadequate education, meager training and only narrow job experience. For example, the present unemployment rate among those with less than five years of schooling is twice the rate for those with a high school education and three times the rate for those with some college training.

The readjustments demanded by technological change can more readily be comprehended and accomplished by a work force both broadly educated as citizens and highly trained as workers. People must face the necessity for geographical and occupational transfers; low levels of education and training limit mobility and increase insecurity. To adapt our labor force to the needs of the new technology, we must further improve our educational standards generally and:

1. Increase substantially the number of scientists, engineers, teachers, doctors and others in the professions;

2. Develop management personnel equipped to understand the social and economic consequences of the new technology, and to adapt technology to the achievement of greater productivity.

3. Expand training programs for technicians, and assistants to engineers and scientists;

4. Upgrade and modernize the skills of craftsmen and other workers;

5. Improve the quality of the elementary and secondary educational systems, giving particular attention to the basic skills of reading and

mathematics which provide the foundation for all later education and training; and thereby make our education adaptable to new techniques.

III. *Modernized Capital Equipment*—Much of the plant and equipment in American industry urgently needs modernization, and automation and technological change are rapidly increasing obsolescence. We are much less productive than we know how to be in many industries. Modernization is particularly required to strengthen the competitive position of American industry in international trade, thereby providing greater employment.

The demand created by a high employment economy would in itself powerfully stimulate modernization. More rapid and realistic depreciation allowances for tax purposes are urgently needed to assist modernization programs. Other countries, particularly those in Western Europe, provide much faster tax write-offs for new equipment than we do. Measures to increase the flow of funds into new plant and equipment are long overdue.

IV. *Improved Employer-Employee Procedures*—Adjustment to technological change cannot be handled adequately in negotiations at the end of a collective bargaining agreement. Experience shows the great value of continuing discussions in which the parties study the effect of technological change on their particular situation. The Armour Automation Committee, the West Coast Longshore Agreement and the Human Relations Committee in Steel are illustrations. Extension of similar procedures can facilitate the acceptance of predictable technological change. They improve communications and encourage both advance notice and manpower planning in a non-crisis atmosphere.

Such continuing reviews should anticipate changes in skills and labor demands, build up the versatility of the work force and cushion readjustments where decreases in employment are involved. Such readjustments will be eased by advance notice, attrition policies, moving allowances, severance allowances, and early retirement.

The parties may also need to re-examine long established practices and contract provisions. Restrictive work practices can best be eliminated by collective bargaining following such review. Furthermore, piece rates, wage incentives or hourly methods of pay may be inappropriate to modern technology in some industries. Broader seniority units will permit senior employees to transfer to other jobs within a plant or a company rather than be laid off. This will require a greater investment in training to enhance versatility.

Some long-established collective bargaining structures may also have to be modified, so that the scope of bargaining better fits the problems at hand. In some cases, this means bringing craft groups together for bargaining purposes; in others, negotiating on particular issues should be decentralized.

Technological change will also create serious problems among technical, professional and management personnel. Many of the policies of communication and versatility suggested for employees represented by unions will also prove helpful for the large number of employees not covered by collective bargaining agreements.

V. *Improved Labor Market Information and Manpower Training*— Technological change involves readjustments in employment as a result both of direct displacement and of competition between an old product or process with the new. These impacts can be mitigated by improving the operation of labor markets as follows:

1. Employment outlook studies in industries and in local communities by private and public agencies should estimate the number of employees and the skills required.

2. Training programs will increase the employability of the unemployed where there is reasonable prospect that they will get jobs as a result of such training, and where they have the requisite aptitude.

3. Guidance and counseling services in schools and industry should give greater attention to increasing versatility.

4. State legislation and administrative rulings which preclude unemployment benefits to workers engaged in approved training programs should be eliminated.

5. Barriers to equal job opportunities arising from race, color, creed or sex should be eliminated. Workers otherwise qualified should not be denied employment solely on account of age.

VI. *Working Hours and Leisure Time*—Gains in productivity in the American economy have in part taken the form of increased leisure. There has been a steady decline in the work week over the past century, although in recent years the trend has often taken the form of paid holidays and vacations. This trend may be expected to continue in particular industries as productivity gains are used for leisure rather than taken in other forms.

Persistent and substantial unemployment is likely to generate insistent demands for general reductions in the work week. Indeed some members of the Assembly favor such a reduction now in selected industries. To most members of the Assembly, however, a general or widespread reduction in hours is not an appropriate measure to mitigate unemployment, since the nation requires a growing output.

How leisure time is used will determine whether technological progress serves cultural, moral and spiritual values as well as material ends. Music, the visual and performing arts and education and community activities are essential.

VIII. *International Aspects*—The emergence of the Common Market, the competition of the communist nations and the awakening of the developing countries all present challenges to the American system. Technology is advancing rapidly abroad. To maintain our higher wage levels and living standards and to meet our foreign commitments we must continue to increase our productivity. Gains of productivity must be allocated to lower prices as well as to higher wages, higher profits and increased leisure; price reductions are a way to preserve and enlarge markets in a competitive world.

International competition places new constraints on many collective bargaining negotiations. Such constraints operate in Western European countries and are likely to be increasingly significant in the United States. In an increasing number of situations the parties cannot neglect these constraints in their own or the national interest. The disparities that may then arise between industries so affected and other industries pose difficult issues for labor markets and collective bargaining.

The United States has skilled people, unused industrial capacity and a wealth of technical and managerial experience which can fruitfully be employed to increase the rate of growth in the developing countries, and in this way not only help to realize abroad important political and moral goals, but also to increase employment and output in the United States.

Participants in the Twenty-first American Assembly

BENJAMIN AARON
Director
Institute of Industrial Relations
University of California
Los Angeles

ALAN E. ADAMS
Business Week
Washington, D.C.

HARRY S. ASHMORE
Editor in Chief
Encyclopaedia Britannica
Chicago

FRANCIS BELLO
Scientific American
New York

JOHN BRADEMAS
Representative from Indiana
Congress of the United States

COURTNEY C. BROWN
Dean
Graduate School of Business Administration
Columbia University

GEORGE A. BROWNELL
Davis, Polk, Wardwell, Sunderland & Kiendl
New York

OTIS BRUBAKER
Director of Research
United Steel Workers of America
Pittsburgh

F. L. BYROM
President
Koppers Company
Pittsburgh

HUGH CALKINS
Jones, Day, Cockley and Reavis
Cleveland

HODDING CARTER, III
Managing Editor
Delta Democrat-Times
Delta, Mississippi

HAROLD CHESTNUT
Senior Control Systems Engineer
General Electric Company
Schenectady

EWAN CLAGUE
United States Commissioner of Labor
  Statistics
Washington, D.C.

CECIL E. COMBS
Major General, USAF
Commandant
Air Force Institute of Technology
Ohio

RICHARD N. COOPER
Council of Economic Advisors
Washington, D.C.

CARL M. CORBIN
Editor
New Orleans States-Item
New Orleans

ROBERT E. DINEEN
Vice President
Northwestern Mutual Life Insurance
  Co.
Milwaukee

L. A. DuBRIDGE
President
California Institute of Technology

JOHN T. DUNLOP
Professor of Economics
Harvard University

ALFRED S. EICHNER
Harriman Scholar
Columbia University

LUTHER H. EVANS
Director, Project on Automation
National Education Association
Washington, D.C.

SIGO FALK
Harbison-Walker Refractories Co.
Pittsburgh

LEWIS P. FREITAS
Harriman Scholar
Columbia University

ELI GINSBERG
Professor of Economics
Columbia University

WILLIAM GLAZIER
International Longshoreman's and
  Warehouseman's Union
San Francisco

JOHN GOCKLEY
Harriman Scholar
Columbia University

LEON GREENBERG
Bureau of Labor Statistics
U. S. Department of Labor
Washington, D.C.

JOHN J. HANSELMAN
American Telephone & Telegraph Co.
New York

A. A. HECKMAN
Executive Director
Hill Foundation
St. Paul

ROY G. HOLLY
Dean
Graduate Faculty
University of Nebraska

CHARLES C. KILLINGSWORTH
Professor of Labor and Industrial Re-
  lations
Michigan State University

ALLAN KLINE
Western Springs, Illinois

G. A. LINCOLN
Colonel, USA
Head, Department of Social Sciences
United States Military Academy
West Point

FREDERICK R. LIVINGSTON
Kaye, Scholer, Fierman, Hays and
  Handler
New York

RUSSELL C. McCARTHY
Industrial Management Council
Rochester

JOHN S. McCAULEY
Director
Manpower Development and Utilization
U. S. Department of Labor
Washington, D.C.

ROBERT F. McDERMOTT
Brigadier General, USAF
Dean of the Faculty
United States Air Force Academy
Colorado

R. D. McGRANAHAN
President
Wilshire Oil Company of California
Los Angeles

FLOYD C. MANN
Institute for Social Research
University of Michigan

WILLIAM B. MILLER
Executive Vice President
Town Hall of Los Angeles

CHARLES A. MYERS
Professor of Industrial Relations
Massachusetts Institute of Technology

LEO R. NEWCOMBE
Vice President
Chicago Sun-Times
Chicago

J. WILSON NEWMAN
Chairman of the Board
Dun and Bradstreet, Inc.
New York

PHIL PEDEN
Judge 157th District Court
Houston

RICHARD E. PILLE
President
Security Mutual Life Insurance Company
Binghamton, New York

E. R. PIORE
Vice President
International Business Machines Corporation
New York

JOHN POST
Director
Industrial and Personnel Relations
Continental Oil Company
Houston

OLLIE A. RANDALL
Vice President
The National Council on the Aging
New York

A. H. RASKIN
Editorial Board
The New York Times
New York

RAYMOND REBSAMEN
Rebsamen and East, Inc.
Little Rock

RALPH REISER
International President
United Glass & Ceramic Workers of North America
Columbus, Ohio

CARL E. REISTLE, Jr.
President
Humble Oil & Refining Company
Houston

EDWIN F. SHELLEY
Vice President
U. S. Industries, Inc.
New York

The American Assembly

American Assembly books are purchased and put to use by thousands of individuals, libraries, businesses, public agencies, non-governmental organizations, educational institutions, discussion meetings and service groups. The subjects of Assembly studies to date are:

1962—AUTOMATION AND TECHNOLOGICAL CHANGE
1961—ARMS CONTROL
   —OUTER SPACE

1960—THE SECRETARY OF STATE
   —THE FEDERAL GOVERNMENT AND HIGHER EDUCATION

   Library, cloth bound edition, $3.95
   Spectrum, paper bound edition, $1.95
   Available from better booksellers and Prentice-Hall, Inc.

The following titles were published by The American Assembly. Prices indicate books which can be obtained by writing to The American Assembly.

1959—THE UNITED STATES AND LATIN AMERICA ($2.00)
   —WAGES, PRICES, PROFITS AND PRODUCTIVITY ($2.00)

1958—THE UNITED STATES AND AFRICA ($2.00)
   —UNITED STATES MONETARY POLICY ($2.00)

1957—ATOMS FOR POWER ($1.00)
   —INTERNATIONAL STABILITY AND PROGRESS

1956—THE UNITED STATES AND THE FAR EAST
   —THE REPRESENTATION OF THE UNITED STATES ABROAD

1955—THE FORTY-EIGHT STATES
   —UNITED STATES AGRICULTURE

1954—THE FEDERAL GOVERNMENT SERVICE
   —THE UNITED STATES STAKE IN THE UNITED NATIONS

1953—ECONOMIC SECURITY FOR AMERICANS

1952—INFLATION

1951—UNITED STATES-WESTERN EUROPE RELATIONSHIPS

Regular readers of The American Assembly receive early copies of each new Assembly study and are billed subsequently. The next Assembly book, to be published by Prentice-Hall, Inc., will be concerned with:

NATIONAL POLICY AND CULTURAL RELATIONS: EDUCATION, SCIENCE, THE ARTS.

To enroll as a regular reader, or for additional information, please address:

The American Assembly, Columbia University, New York 27, New York.